PEOPLE 101

GETTING AN A
IN RELATIONSHIPS

*Thanks for the
support!*
Lawrence Alexander

LAWRENCE ALEXANDER

CONTENTS

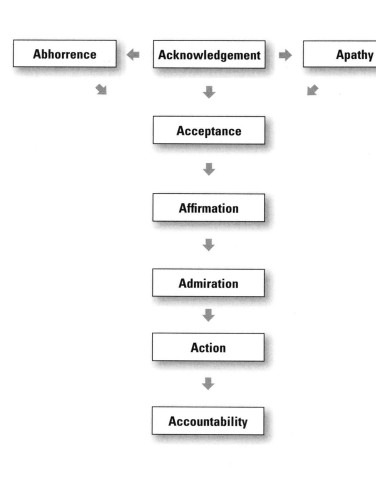

PREFACE

IN 1995, I read Stu Weber's excellent book *Locking Arms – God's Design For Masculine Friendships*. In the book he described four masculine relationship milepost consisting of Acceptance, Affirmation, Accountability, and Authority. His book left a definite impression on me. In 1998, I started an adventure-based teambuilding organization called Challenge Point. Through the following years, I worked with several groups on relationships. During that time I created my own version of relationship stages based off of Mr. Weber's original four. This is not an effort to better an idea. It is simply the product of precious seeds sown. After years of giving this talk at retreats, I decided to put it down in ink.

In some ways this book is written as two books in one. For those who are interested in the simple academics of the eight stages, I suggest reading chapters five and eight. Those two chapters contain the meat of the message. For those who want a story to go along with it, the rest of the book was written for you. I always enjoy a good story or experience to help me understand a concept and I hope that is what this book accomplishes.

Chapter 1

ABHORRENCE

Monday - June 11, 1990
8:52 PM
Some town, Somewhere

ALEX sat at his desk in his room looking at the ever growing pile of pamphlets and brochures he had received from colleges throughout the nation. They all screamed of glorious reasons why he should spend the next four years upon their magnificent campuses. He had already flipped through them all umpteen times and made no decision, even though his time to do so was growing thin. No matter how promising the brochure, still nothing magnetized him as much as his fully stocked backpack in the corner of his room.

Originally, he and his father were going to take the summer after his graduation and hike the Southern Forks Trail. The western terminus of the 500 mile trail was just a few miles from his house, and so growing up, he had always dreamed of making the trek. During the journey he would make all the important decisions that would shape his life for the next ten years. Those plans were violently derailed when his father up and left last January. Every encounter with his family since then had been evermore brutal as his parents fought over matters concerning the divorce. Graduation had occurred two-weeks ago and now all of his plans for the future were seen through a veil of whether he should flee or stay and protect what was left of his family.

With frustration building, he finally grabbed all the brochures and slung them into his garbage can. Then, more symbolically than anything, he jerked his pack up and slammed it into the garbage as well. He fell back onto his bed and was about to burst into tears when he heard his mother yell, "Your Dad just pulled up and he's angry!"

Alex remained in his room and gripped his pillow. Soon he heard the slamming of the front door and then a loud kicking until finally the door crashed inward. The sound of his mother screaming followed by the roar of his father were soon met with the unmistakable clash of fist on face. Alex sprang from his bedroom in the base-ment and raced up the stairs just in time to tackle his father. As the two hit the ground a pistol fell from some-where hidden on his father and slid across the floor. Alex looked up to see his mother pick it up and point it at her soon to be ex. Looking into her eyes, he could tell sanity had left her several punches ago. Quickly he sprang up over his fallen father and snatched the gun from her hand. Not knowing what to do, he ran out the broken door and into the side yard. There, in the moonlight he stopped as his heart raced. *What now? How did it get to this point?*

Before he could rationalize anything sensible he looked up to see his father walking along the front porch, dragging his mother by her hair. He stood and watched as the brute slung her off the porch and onto the rock-laden driveway. With scratched up elbows and knees she looked back at him and screamed twenty years of hatred. Her husband's response was quick and sparked by rage. He jumped off the porch and hoisted the largest rock he could find. Raising it above his head, he was about to end the fight forever when a cry from his son stopped him. Alex had instinctively raised the pistol and aimed it at his father's chest. "Put the rock down now!"

For a second the older man looked into his son's eyes and he knew it was no bluff. Carefully he lowered the rock to the ground and backed away from his crying wife. With the gun aimed and ready to fire, Alex kept it on his father until he had retreated back to his truck and driven away. He then watched his mother escape back into the house. Not knowing what to do, he took the gun and walked into the woods behind his house. As a child he had discovered a hollow tree and kept his boyhood treasures there. Now, he used it as a place to discard an evil he never wanted to experience again.

Alex took his time returning to his house, but when he did the scene had completely changed. The police were there along with his aunt and a couple of his mother's closet friends. When his aunt saw him return, she rushed up to him and gave him a hug. "It's not safe here anymore. You are coming home with me."

"Your place is no safer. Dad will find her there and do the same thing."

"I simply said you are coming with me. Your Mom has already left. She is going someplace safe where she can get help. It may be awhile before we see her again."

Alex stood there for a second letting it all sink in. He was over eighteen and knew the next move was completely his own. "Do you need help gathering your belongings?"

Alex looked back with a smile like he had just found the exit door in hell, "No. I just need my backpack."

"Your backpack?"

"Yep. That's all I will need on the trail."

Thursday - May 27, 2010
4:35 PM
Brookhaven Community

Bam! Bam! Bam! The thin door shook with each blow.

"Matthew! What are you doing in there?"

In utter shock, the ruddy headed teen turned to the other two people in his darkly lit, disheveled bedroom. His compromised cohorts were staring back with panicked wide-eyes. "I thought your parents were gone!"

"They are," Matthew replied as he frantically began erasing any signs of what had just occurred. "It's my…"

Suddenly the door gave way and in walked Matthew's older brother. Within a single glance of the room the big guy drew a picture of what had just happened and then glared back in absolute anger. "Get out of our house!" he screamed at Matthew's accomplices. The frightened teens grabbed their belongings and dashed for the door. With their heads down, whether in shame or in fear that they might receive a fist to the face, they dove through the door and took off. Now it was just Matthew and his brother.

"You can't tell Mom and Dad. They wouldn't understand."

"They wouldn't understand? The only thing I understand is you're sick!"

"Please…" pleaded Matthew with tears in his eyes. "I won't do it again. Please…I'm your brother!"

"My brother? You are not my brother! There is no way a catastrophic disappointment like you could share the same blood as me! I hate you!"

As rage and disgust poured from his brother's face, Matthew searched his mind for something to say to make it alright, but in the end the only word he could muster was a feeble plea, "Please?"

"Get out of my face!"

Unable to look his brother in his eyes any more, Matthew turned, left the house and walked out into the darkness.

Thursday - May 27, 2010
8:35 PM
Johnson High School

The night enveloped the oval, running track, quietly putting to sleep all but one sentimental onlooker. Caleb had ruled this domain for the past two years, setting the high school record in the 200 and 400. Tomorrow night he and his graduating class would meet in the center under the stadium lights for one final commencement ceremony. Tonight though, the track was his alone.

The blonde-haired athlete was fast enough to shine at several small colleges, and he had received some partial scholarships to a few. In the grand scheme of things though, they mattered not. His course had already been set long before was been born. He would be attending the same state university from which three generations of his family had graduated – the same university where his parents had met. It was the largest school in the state and any athletic endeavors would be more difficult to achieve. His mother was his biggest fan and a strong believer that he would excel. He lacked her unwavering enthusiasm, so tonight he slipped on his white spikes one last time for a final lap as a champion.

The moon lit his way as he took his position. *On your mark…get set…* With a powerful kick, Caleb burst into a sprint flying through the first 100 meters. Settling into his stride, for the next 200 meters he relaxed and embraced the feel of the wind in his face and the rhythm of his feet striking the track. Memories of his past conquests flooded his mind. He smiled as he recalled the looks of shock and frustration on the faces of his opponents as he flew past them. He could hear the fans cheering his name. *"Caleb! Caleb! Caleb!"*

For the final 100 meters he popped it into sixth gear one last time and soared to the finish line raising his hands in victory, then resting them on his head as he caught his breath. "The final run of Caleb Willia…aaaaah!"

The first kidney punch came out of nowhere and paralyzed him with shooting pain. The second blow was to his gut, knocking his breath out and dropping him to his knees. It was the kick across his chest though that put him on his back. From his lowered position he looked up to see five guys looming over him. One in particular caught his eye. "Max?"

"Wow Caleb. I didn't know you knew who I was, since I spent the last two years ten feet behind you."

"Is this some kind of joke, because it's not funny?"

"Ha!" laughed Max just before he kicked Caleb in the ribs. "Then let me tell you a joke that is funny...my track career! Of course I didn't know what a joke it was until I applied for scholarships. It seems no one wants the second fastest!"

"Max it's not that you're too slow to receive a scholarship, it's that you're too stupid!" With a swift swing of his leg, Caleb kicked the feet out from under one of Max's goons. As fast as his oppressor hit the ground, Caleb hopped to his feet. He made it about two steps before Max's mini-mob knocked him to the ground once again. The next few minutes were a medley of kicks and punches while Caleb helplessly curled into a ball and endured the pain. The beating came to a climax when one of the brutes picked up a rod and was about to strike him. That's when Max reached in and stopped him.

"I don't want anything too critical to keep him from showing up at graduation tomorrow with his black eyes and bloody lip."

Having accomplished their mission, they left Caleb on the side of the track bruised and bloody. He lay there for some time, not because of the damage to his body though. When he finally did get up and hobble to his car, the drive home felt even longer.

"Honey, is that you?" called his mother as he walked in the door and headed up the stairs to his bedroom to hide.

"Yeah, I'm home."

"You got home just in time. Can you come help me pick up some groceries in town? It seems the entire extended family is coming to your graduation party. Caleb?"

"What Mom?"

"Are you coming to help me?"

"No! Leave me alone!"

Friday - May 28, 2010
10:40 PM
Two miles from Big State University

"Aren't you driving a bit fast, Andrea?"

"Oh please, Lance. If you can't deal with my driving, are you sure you're up for this mission?"

"I have no doubt about my expert yard rolling skills," touted the fair-complected drama king. "I am the absolute best at the Christian Student Center. They don't call me Mr. TP for nothing. My only concern is will I make it there alive!"

"Well I can assure you I've been driving for almost four years now, which is probably longer than you've been using toilet paper, my little Mississippi boy."

"Touché, my young Guinevere, touché"

"Can someone back there slap Lance...a lot?" The

unlucky sap was sitting between Claire and Stephanie, two girls who were fully capable of crushing him if they saw fit. Fortunately for him they both simply giggled and popped him upside his head.

"Ow! That was in stereo," winced Lance.

Jess, who had been Andrea's best friend and roommate from the first week they had started college, was sitting in the front passenger seat. She turned around to view the lone guy squished between the two ladies, "You are such a goof. Why are you with us again?"

"I helped Rick roll Andrea's house last year, so in an effort to be fair, I'm helping her this time around."

Jess rolled her eyes and then looked square at Andrea, "He doesn't know yet, does he?"

"Know what?"

"You are so dense," snapped Jess. "Andrea and Rick broke up and now we're rolling someone else's yard."

"Someone else? Who?"

"Lisa Hastings."

"Lisa? Why Lisa?"

The car suddenly swerved on the road as Andrea turned to look him in the eyes. Jess grabbed the wheel as Andrea melted Lance with her stare. "You really are that dense." She took the wheel back and soon they pulled into Lisa's neighborhood. Andrea pulled the car over in a dark section of the road a few houses down from Lisa's and turned off the lights. "Let's do this."

Quietly they got out and gathered their goods. Lance snagged the heftiest bag of toilet paper and took off down the road. By the time the ladies reached Lisa's yard, it looked like Christmas had arrived. "He really is good," smiled Jess.

"As our campus minister says, 'Everyone has a special gift.'" Claire and Stephanie giddily took their rolls and ran to join Lance.

"Why did we bring the dumpling twins?" asked Jess.

"Because they fear me and can keep a secret," smiled Andrea as she pulled out a can of spray paint.

"Isn't that slightly more permanent than our original plan called for?"

"No more permanent than her stealing my boyfriend, sneered Andrea while Jess looked on hesitantly. "You are my best friend, aren't you?"

"Of course."

"Then I know I have your support."

Jess sighed and then grinned as she picked up a can of spray paint, "That is what true friends are for."

Lance stood in the backyard admiring his handiwork while Claire and Stephanie finished off one last dogwood. "That is nothing short of masterful."

"Keep it down," whispered Stephanie.

"There's no one here, replied Lance. "I watched you bounce a roll off the window up there. It was such a thud it would have awakened the dead."

"In that case, let's get out of here before we get caught," declared Claire as she finished off the last roll. The trio walked around front looking for Jess and Andrea when they saw them up near the front door.

"What are they doing?" asked Lance.

"Oh my…" gasped Stephanie as she shone her light

on the word 'whore' written in bright red letters along the driveway.

"It gets worse," said Lance whose light now shone on the street where a large arrow pointing to the house was accompanied by colorful expletives.

"I didn't know there were so many ways to write that word."

Chapter 2

APATHY

Tuesday – June 5, 1990
_2:51 PM_
Some office, Somewhere

WILLIAM sat back in his chair with his feet on his desk and watched the clock on the wall tick away. In just a few minutes he would be walking into a room where he would spend the next hour trying to convince a group of hopeless individuals on a self-destructive path that they needed to change their ways.

During the process they would remind him that he is half their age with no true life experience beyond the hollow degree he spent four years in academia to post on his wall. He had never struggled with drugs, nor been married or divorced, nor had raised any kids of his own. He had never had a near-death experience or suffered from an incurable disease transmitted from a dirty needle. He had never been incarcerated or even chased by the police.

What they didn't know and he would never reveal is that his parents had left him to be raised by his grandmother and that she had just died last month. He would never let them know that all of his closest friends had graduated and moved away and that most of his evenings and nights were spent alone. They didn't know he too was broken and wounded, and he would never tell.

Five minutes before the hour struck, William stood up, collected his folders and walked out the door. He journeyed down the hall and into the meeting room where twenty eyes apathetically stared him down. Whatever hope he brought with him was drained within the first minute. The other 59 were dedicated to devouring the soul.

At the end of the hour, William walked out without his folders and instead of heading back to his office, he drug his feet without care down to his supervisor's office. His supervisor had been here for years and as soon as she looked up into William's hopeless eyes she knew what was coming next. "I quit." And with that William walked out the door.

Thursday - May 27, 2010
8:48 PM
A few miles outside Brookhaven Community

Matthew wiped the remaining tears from his eyes as he looked at yet another intimidating door. The night was turning cold and he knew his chances were diminishing. With a final sigh, he marched up the steps and knocked on the door. A few seconds passed, and then a woman opened the door. "May I help you?"

"Is Brian home?"

She nodded and turned away, "Brian you have company." In time a tall, lanky teen stood at the door with an awkward look on his face. "Matthew? Matthew Herron?"

"It's Matthew Harris. I sat behind you in Geometry last semester."

"Okay…If you came to get a Geometry assignment, I have to tell you it's a little late."

"Ha…no," Matthew nervously laughed. "I was in the neighborhood and wondered if you wanted to hang out."

"Hang out?" Brian glanced over Matthew's shoulder. "Where's your car? How did you get here?"

"Oh, I walked."

"Don't you live in Brookhaven?"

"Yeah."

"That's about three miles away."

"Four actually. So, do you want to hang out? I'm even free to spend the night if you would like."

Brian looked back awkwardly. "Matthew I'm afraid this isn't a good time. My family has big plans for me tomorrow and I had better turn in early tonight. Sorry." With that said, the big red door slammed shut and the porch light turned off, leaving Matthew alone and in the dark once again. It was the seventh door he had knocked on, and the six prior had had the same result.

Out of ideas, he wandered back down the road. *I can't believe this is happening to me. Heck! I can't believe I got caught. By now my parents know…They'll disown me. I thought my friends would come to my rescue, but I guess I was wrong. I've been wrong about a lot of things. I can't believe John wouldn't let me stay at his place. We've been going to church and school together since kindergarten. He didn't even have an excuse. Neither did Jason or Chad or Phillip. They just said they didn't have time. What they should have said is they really don't care…*

Lost in his thoughts, Matthew meandered his way downtown towards the homeless shelter where he and his brother had volunteered on a few occasions. It was an area of town where he never pictured himself being after nightfall, but somehow the situation seemed to fit with the sequence of the night. He knew the layout of the shelter and he figured if he was smooth enough, he could sneak in without being recognized and find a cot for the night He was still working on his strategy when an old, beat-up Buick drove up next to him.

"Hey! Aren't you Bolt's little brother?" He turned to see four senior high guys staring back from a smoke filled cab.

"Who's asking?"

"Don't act like you don't know us, punk. What are you doing out here?"

"Nothing," mumbled Matthew.

"Nothing?" laughed the driver. "That ends now. We can't have Bolt's little bro wandering around in the dark. Jump in!"

Matthew froze. *You've never paid me any attention*

before. My parents don't approve of you. Of course,
they probably don't approve of me either...

"Hey! Are you getting in or not?"

While his brain was still stuck in the decision making
process, his hand reached out and opened the back door
while his legs provided the spring to jump in. The whole
process was still surreal to him as the car squealed its
wheels and took off.

"This is freakin hilarious man!" laughed the heavily
intoxicated fellow sharing the backseat with Matthew.
"Bolt couldn't make it tonight, but we end up with his
brother! You've got some big shoes to fill," he said as
he handed him a beer. Scared of what might happen
next, Matthew took the bottle and meagerly sipped it.
The taste sent him into reflexive gagging. "Not bad, but
not Bolt!" exclaimed the drunk as he slapped Matthew
on the back. "Your brother spewed it on his first try!
Remember that night, Cujo?"

"I remember," laughed the guy from the front
passenger seat. "My hair smelled sour the rest of the
night!" Cujo let the hearty laugh play itself out as he
seemed to drift away deep in thought of grandeur days.
Then, just as if the movie had ended he awoke with an
evil grin. "Well with Bolt officially represented, we now
have the whole gang together and can commence with
tonight's activities." Cujo then reached under his seat
and pulled out a gun. Matthew didn't know what type,
only that it was a pistol. "Little Matthew let me introduce you to your brother's favorite toy. Your brother
actually whipped another punk and stole it from him.
Your brother was something else! Too bad he's not here!

Let's go hunting boys!" exclaimed Cujo as he fired away at an oncoming car. Frozen in fear, Matthew sank into the backseat while the shots rang out.

Friday - August 27, 2010
6:35 PM
Christian Student Center
at Big State University

The two-story brick building was old and run down. The shutters were desperate for a paint job as were the porch columns. The dilapidated structure served as an odd backdrop for the colorful cookout spread across the sunny green lawn. A big banner saying, "Welcome Freshmen" accompanied several picnic tables covered in a bountiful spread of hamburgers, hotdogs, potato salad, and baked beans.

Caleb stood on the sidewalk staring at this new circle of possibilities as he battled with the decision to step into it. He had been at the university for almost a week and had made few acquaintances. The past couple of months had been emotionally tough and his social ego was a bit bruised. It had been his hope that visiting the Christian Student Center would be a place of healing.

With a deep breath he put on his best smile and stepped off the sidewalk and into the green grass. There was a large crowd of college students made up of several small gatherings. In an effort to fit in, he made himself a plate of food and then casually meandered his way into a close knit group of four girls and three guys. Upon his entrance, there was a slight pause in the conversation before it continued on. Caleb tried to understand the topic so he could join in, but since it was all about their hatred towards someone he didn't know, he soon gave up and wandered into the next group. Changing his tactics, he found a guy with a nametag and introduced himself. "Hey Lance. My name's Caleb."

Lance stared at him for a second as he looked him over. "You a freshman?"

"Yeah…Just arrived last week."

Lance looked at him like he gave the wrong answer and then turned his back to him. "Anyway, as I was saying…"

Caleb moved on, only to bounce from one small gathering to the next, like a pinball. *I can be this alone back in my dorm room.* With that final thought, he gave up on the game, tossed his paper plate in the garbage and headed back to his dorm. Just as he was about to step back on the sidewalk, he heard the voice of a girl call out, "Hey! Where are you going?" He turned around only to hear, "Oh…I thought you were someone…"

"Else?" replied Caleb. "Someone else?"

"Right," she snipped and walked off.

The campus minister and his assistant watched the entire incident from their viewpoint on the porch. As the minister watched Caleb leave, he called the girl over. "Andrea, can you come here for a moment?"

"Sure, Mr. George. What can I do for you?"

"Who was that gentlemen you just spoke with? The one who just left."

"I didn't know him," she replied innocently.

"You never asked his name?"

"No. Why?"

Mr. George simply looked at her in confusion. "Since you didn't know him, it never occurred to you to ask his name?"

"Why would I do that? This is a big university. I can't know everyone."

"Never mind, Andrea." While she trotted on back to her friends, Mr. George just shook his head. "What have I gotten myself into?"

"What do you mean?" asked his assistant, Carl.

"I realize I've only been here a few months and I have much to do, but I doubt we can reach any of our spiritual goals until the students learn the basics of relationships."

"Do I foresee you preaching a long line of sermons about David and Jonathan for the next semester?"

"No, not me. I'll be calling in a friend for this one. In the meantime, I need to find out the name of that boy, along with the dozens of others who left friendless today."

Carl scratched his head and nodded. "I don't know about the dozens, but I did recognize the guy Andrea snubbed. That was the Williams boy."

"Williams boy?"

"Don't you watch the news?" asked Carl in surprise. "He and his family were all over the tube a couple months ago."

"Oh my!" expressed Mr. George. "That's Caleb Williams. We need to reach that kid."

Friday - September 10, 2010
4:35 PM
The Track at Big State University

The robust track coach stood at the finish line of the 100 meter dash with his stop watch in hand. "Push it! Give it all you got!" he yelled as five guys ultimately sprinted past him. Daniel, the leader of the pack crossed the line and then tripped on his own foot. The result was an acrobatic crash to the ground. "You alright, son?"

Daniel hopped up with a scraped knee and elbow along with a scuffed brow. "I'm good coach."

"What's your name #14?"

"Daniel Harris, sir."

"What high school are you from?"

"Oak Hill High in Brookhaven, sir."

"I know Oak Hill," said the coach as he massaged his turkey neck. "That's Coach Schmidt's school. He never mentioned you."

"I didn't run in high school, sir."

"So how did you get so fast?"

"I was busy surviving on the other side of the track."

"Well, welcome to my track," said the coach with a quick smile before turning stern again and facing the other runners. "Guys I appreciate all of you coming out this week and showing me your best effort. While you take one final cool down lap, I'll post the results on the wall. Remember, if you made the team, be here next Monday at 3 PM."

That moment froze in Daniel's mind. It was the first time in five days that the coach had even acknowledged his presence. To be honest, the whole experience of trying out for the team had been a lonely one. From the moment he had arrived on Monday the coach had run them ragged. Between sprints there had been little time for chit chat as they all struggled to catch their breath and prepare for the next hurdle. Daniel had always been somewhat of a loner; never one to initiate conversation. Seeing those around him as competitors and not as comrades fit rather nicely with the persona he had created and lived in high school. All of this though went against his initial reason for joining the team. Loneliness was comfortable, but he wanted more. He just wasn't sure about the next step.

As Daniel joined the twenty other hopefuls in a jog around the track, his eyes wandered to the stadium where a sole onlooker remained. Through the whole four day trial the young man had been there in the same spot watching intently. *Who are you? You never wave at anyone. You never talk to...* Suddenly at that moment the guy looked Daniel straight in the eyes and waved.

"Is that your boyfriend?" laughed one of the runners.

"I don't know who he is," replied Daniel. "Do you?"

The guy laughed, "I'm from Idaho. I don't know anyone. Max, do you know him?"

A spike-haired fellow that had quietly run near the front of the pack throughout the week suddenly emerged from the crowd. He looked up into the stands and then directly into the eyes of Daniel. "His name is Caleb Williams and if he were down here on the track you would all know him."

Hearing the name sent a cold chill down Daniel's spine. "See you guys at the wall," he said as he sped up leaving the others behind. He practically sprinted the last stretch so that when he reached the wall, only the senior members of the team were circled around the list of those who had made the cut. They had been there all week watching. As Daniel approached, they parted the way, allowing him to walk directly up to the posting. He perused the listings until he found his number and name. "Looks like I'm part of the team," he smiled confidently to the seniors. "When does the initiation stage and welcome party begin? I'm all ready for the blindfold walks and naked runs across campus."

The seniors looked back with little emotion. "Coach may have chosen you, but we didn't."

Daniel took a step back, then responded, "Well, like it or not, I'm on your team."

Now a guy named Reed was the head senior and at that moment he rushed in stopping an inch from Daniel's nose, "Get this through your thick skull, we don't like you! And no matter how Coach feels about you, our feelings are not going to change. We don't care about you or any of the other newbies. You're nothing more than road kill." And with that declaration, Reed and his team walked off.

Chapter 3

ACKNOWLEDGEMENT

Saturday – June 16, 1990
6:48 PM
Southern Fork Trail

FOR three days it had rained without ceasing, and that's a lot considering Alex had only been on the trail for four days. There was nothing on him that wasn't soaked. Of course, he had a rain jacket and rain cover for his pack, but with all the sweating and setting up camp and taking it back down in rain, the feeling of being dry had become a lost memory.

Beyond being wet, the trail had also proven to be somewhat lonely. In the last four days he had seen only a few other hikers and due to the weather, conversation had become minimal. Most were older individuals who he passed and never saw again. With his heart and mind at war, he really had not been upset with having some time to himself to think. This evening though, with the rain finally coming to an end, he began to wonder how long it would be until he started having complete conversations with himself.

It was now almost seven and way past time to find a campsite. He had continued on hoping to find the perfect spot just around the bend, but was about to give in, when he caught the smell of smoke from up ahead. Alex picked up his pace and soon discovered a lone hammock set up next to a sizzling campfire. Desperately needing to get warm and dry, Alex took a closer look. "Hello? Anyone home?"

From a nearby creek walked a young man, probably five-years older than Alex. "Hello! You looked soaked. "

"I'm beyond soaked."

"Well, join me for camp. I could use some help keeping this fire going."

"That I can do. Alexander George at your service. You can call me Alex."

"Alexander George? Do you realize your first name is a last name and your last name is a first name?"

"Yeah...What can I say? Cruel parents. And you are?"

"The name is William, William Barrow?"

"You mean to tell me your name is Will Barrow?"

"Yeah...Cruel parents."

Tuesday – August 24, 2010
3:55 PM
Sunrise Youth Development Center

At best the cinder block room was 5x7 with an uncomfortable bed, an open toilet, a swiveling metal chair bolted to the floor and a bare desk with two drawers built into the wall. There were no windows except for the small Plexiglas slit in the metal door that remained locked most hours of the day. Matthew had been in the juvenile detention center for three days now and remained on new orientation lock-down.

He had spent numerous days in a county jail prior to this while the court dates had dragged on. While there he had been surrounded by prostitutes, drug dealers and essentially every version of societal villainy. At the time, he considered it the worst situation imaginable, but after almost 72 hours of basic solitude he missed the questionable company. *How did I get to this point? I didn't even...*

Suddenly his thoughts were interrupted by the loud sound of the door being unlocked followed by a guard stepping through. "Matthew Harris, you have a date with your counselor. Follow me." Happy to leave the tight quarters, Matthew did as ordered. The guard marched him through the community quarters of his quad where quite a few residents took a look at the newbie. The attention was beyond uncomfortable for Matthew as he felt the unfriendly eyes sizing him up. To his relief the distance was short and soon the guard pulled out his radio and ordered the next locked door open. He then led Matthew off the quad and down a long hall until finally stopping at a door and giving it a polite knock.

"Come in!"

The guard opened the door. "I have Matthew Harris here, as you requested."

"Send him in. I'll call you when I'm done with him." At the guards urging, Matthew walked into the office to see a middle-aged man in casual dress, winding an old tin pocket watch. He seemed to get the watch just as he wanted, then looked up. "Have a seat Matthew. My name is Mr. Barrow and I will be your counselor here during your stay at Sunrise Youth Development Center, a.k.a. the Pen. Now, before you open your mouth and say something stupid, let me just share with you that our relationship begins right now. Everything you say and do from this point onward will impact that relationship and it is important that this relationship works well."

Not truly knowing what to say Matthew managed to utter a feeble, "Alright."

"Now let me stop you right there," continued Mr. Barrow. "The one commodity that you will want here, more than anything, is respect. The way you will get it, is to give it and needless to say it is crucial to your progress here."

"Yes sir," replied Matthew.

"That's better," smiled the counselor as he pulled a file out of his desk and opened it. "Now let's see what got you here."

"I'm one of the Brookhaven bravos...sir."

"Yes, rather infamous group, I must say. You were involved in a shooting spree through three counties, injuring twelve and killing two. According to my records, the other three participants are looking at life in prison. The only reason you didn't end up in the same boat as them, is your juvenile age and the fact they covered for you, saying you never touched the gun. It seems we have lots to talk about."

Monday – September 6, 2010
8:45 am
Big State University

"Just because the sign say stop, doesn't mean you have to stop forever!" The torrential downpour on this particular Monday morning just added to the stress Andrea felt on any typical day she had to fight for a parking space on the maddening traffic-packed campus. The fact that she had gotten no sleep the night before just amplified her usual frantic anger into certifiable madness.

"Get out of my way, you moron!" she screamed as she lay down on her horn. After a few questionable traffic maneuvers, several shrieking obscenities with accompanied hand gestures, and one intense game of chicken, she found her parking space. Now began the second leg of the trek as she gathered her many belongings, popped her pretty purple umbrella and quickly pranced her way to class.

"Did you hear the latest news?" Andrea's lips had been on the brink of bursting off her face all morning as she anticipated telling her personal social club. Like a good ringleader, she had selected, united and shaped her dream team into just the kind of circle that would feed her social needs. "Lisa and Rick broke up!" She would have called them late last night when she learned the news, but telling them face to face just before their first class of the day was so much more enjoyable.

"How do you know? Not that you wouldn't know. You know most everything," blabbed a freshman girl who worshipped the ground Andrea walked on.

"She told us this would happen," agreed a second girl even more snotty than the first.

"I have my sources," replied Andrea as she pretended to not hear the praise they lavished on her. "The important thing is that Rick came to the realization that there is no substitute for moi."

"As if there ever was any doubt," stated the second girl. "You are so much prettier than Lisa." This began a competition of praise at the foot of Andrea's throne. She sat there and soaked it up as other students hurried in for class. Nearly a hundred students were taking the freshman Psychology class. Andrea had failed it three years ago and was repeating it now to graduate. Watching them fill the room she went about her usual assessment. *"You're a lonely geek; you're a dumb jock, but nicely built; he's a prancing pretty boy, she's country virgin; computer nerd; thumb-sucking momma's boy; she's a psycho-emo, junkie two-face skank, ghetto... what are you?*

Andrea's stereotyping had been interrupted by the presence of a young lady wearing a black scarf across her face. Nothing else about the girl stood out, only the scarf. "What's up with the scarf?" When Andrea snapped the question across the room, everyone turned to look at her and then to the target of the inquiry. The girl with the scarf froze as she felt the weight of the stares. Her head was down, but slowly she raised it to look directly at Andrea. "Are you Muslim because those ghetto pants don't scream religious?!" Whether the girl was ever to respond, no one will ever know, because Andrea's troop jumped on the band wagon.

"Those pants are so last decade!"

"And if I was going to commit a fashion crime by wearing a scarf, I would at least wear one that didn't look so cheap!" The young lady dropped her eyes to the ground and unconsciously reached up and touched her scarf. "That's right!" continued the berating. "If it comes three in a pack at the dollar store it's officially cheap!" The final words were too much for the girl to bear. She raced out of the room.

Andrea just shook her head, "Looks like some people can't handle the truth."

Sunday – September 12, 2010
6:45 PM
Big State University

Daniel knew the chair was big, that's why it had always been his favorite. Its fluffy arms and oversized cushions had been a welcome joy to sink into after a long day at school. But now, as he had it lodged between the stairwell railing somewhere between the third and fourth floor of his dormitory, it seemed more like a bulky monstrosity. *Let's see...if I can wedge that leg up and turn the chair up on its side...* Daniel maneuvered his footing to two different steps and squatted placing his hands under the wedged leg. With all his effort he lifted, but to no avail. Red faced, he stood back up and scratched his head.

"Newbie, you are in our way!" Daniel looked up to see three of the senior track guys coming down the stairs, and at a rapid speed. Before he could react they were on him. Actually, they were on the chair like a trampoline and then they grabbed the railing and bounced off Daniel. The first two kicked him back into the corner of the stairwell, but Daniel's reactions were fast and he managed to snag the third guy's pants just below the knee. What happened next was a three-man domino show that ended in a pile up on the next landing.

While the tripped-up trio struggled back onto their feet, Daniel's impulse was to run. Instinctual flight had saved his life several times in his teen years. But this time, whether the fact he didn't want to leave his chair, or because he didn't want to live the same old life, he stayed his ground and faced his foes. Two of the seniors managed to stand up while the third remained huddled in the corner grasping his ankle. As Daniel stood there with his chest out gritting his teeth, the seniors looked as if they were about to pounce, but then pulled back. "We'll deal with you later." They then turned and left, leaving their fallen comrade to limp off by himself.

With a deep breath, Daniel finally relaxed. It was only then that he realized someone was standing just behind him. He recognized him immediately and tensed up even more than before. "They're a friendly lot," said the young man.

"They had it in for me even before today," replied Daniel.

"Of course they do. They know you're faster than them and that you're about to shake up their little hierarchy."

Now Daniel knew who he was, but still did his best

to not reveal that fact. "You watched us this past week at the track?"

"I did. My name's Caleb. And you're number 14."

"Yes, but you can call me Daniel, especially since you just saved my hide."

Caleb smiled, "Oh no problem. I actually enjoyed giving them the evil eye. Besides, I've been outnumbered in a fight and it's no fun."

"Well, thank you," replied Daniel as they shook hands. "Just let me know how I can pay you back."

"How about you let me help you move the Titanic here? I'm terribly bored and maneuvering tacky furniture through stairwells happens to be one of my favorite hobbies."

Daniel looked at him and started laughing. "Far be it from me to stomp on your dreams."

Tuesday – September 14, 2010
9:28 PM
Christian Student Center
at Big State University

Tuesday night's singing and devotional at the Christian Student Center had always been Lisa's favorite part of the week. Tonight though, she had barely managed to get through it without crying. Where once she had enjoyed the warmth of smiling faces while listening to the joyous harmony of uplifted praises, now she had felt a barrage of ill looks along with a hissing of foul whispers.

Lisa had always been shy. Ever since her first appearance at the campus ministry over a year ago she had hidden in the corners and shadows far from the center of the crowd; the only exception being when Rick had stepped in and bolstered her confidence. But, those days were gone. After the way she had been treated the past few weeks she wanted nothing more than to leave after the devotional, but tonight she had one final farewell to say.

Mr. George almost didn't notice her as the final clump of college students filed out of the front doors of the Center. He had walked into his office and picked up a few personal items to take home when he turned around to see her slumped head looking up at him with trepid eyes. "Mr. George?"

"Yes, Lisa. What may I do for you?"

"I'm sorry to bother you..."

"Talking to you is no bother. It is an honor," he said with a warm smile. "Come, sit down."

Lisa sheepishly did as she was asked and then took a deep breath. "Mr. George I'm here because you and my uncle are such good friends. I felt I should tell you personally."

"Tell me what Lisa?"

"This is my last night to be involved with the Christian Student Center. I'm afraid I won't be back."

Now it was Mr. George's time to take a deep breath. "This has to do with Andrea and Rick, right?" Lisa nodded while looking at the floor. "Rick isn't to blame. He was very nice to me...perhaps too nice."

"What do you mean?"

"Oh, it was nothing bad," she said with a touch of alarm. "He was always a perfect gentleman. It's just that rumors started swirling that we were dating, which we weren't! Anyway, his ex didn't like it and it seems several others didn't either. My house was trashed a few weeks ago. I was hoping that was the end of it, but…but… I no longer feel welcome here. I don't know if you've noticed, but Rick hasn't been here in two weeks."

"Yes, I've noticed."

"He got tired of the drama."

Mr. George sighed deeply. "It certainly has been drama around here ever since Rick and Andrea broke up. I mean, there was always drama, but it exploded at that point. I'm sorry you got pulled into the middle of it. Is your house ok?"

"Most of it was harmless. There was some graffiti on the house that required a fresh coat of paint and a stretch along the driveway that took a whole Saturday to scrub off."

"I'm so sorry about that," shared Mr. George. "I do have a plan to change the attitude around here, part of which has to do with your uncle. I am looking for a student to be one of my point people in this project though. Rick was my usual go-to-guy on this, but now that he is gone…"

Almost an hour later, Lisa left the Center and headed down the sidewalk with a stack of flyers in her arms. A myriad of thoughts swirled in her head stirred by excitement and doubt. *Why did he choose me? Why not one of the guys who leads singing or speaks at the devotionals? They're much better at dealing with people. No one even notices…*

Suddenly Lisa collided with another student. The

impact sent Lisa crashing down on her tush while launching flyers high into the air. As usual, her head had been down, and therefore she had never seen him coming. But now, with her eyes wide open looking upward at the papers flying everywhere, she saw a young man rush to help her up. "I'm so sorry!" he quickly apologized while struggling to catch his breath. As he helped her to her feet, over his shoulder she saw a small mob of guys rushing upon the scene. The moment they saw the commotion of the collision they backed off into the shadows. "I was in a rush and didn't even see you," continued the apologetic guy.

"Most people don't," responded Lisa as she hurriedly tried to recover the flyers.

"Don't what?" replied the guy as he joined in to help her. "Don't crash into you?"

"No, I mean…yes…Oh never mind."

The guy looked at her confused. "Anyway, I would have noticed you had I not been a bit preoccupied," he said as he looked back at the seniors looming in the distance.

"Friends of yours?"

"Friends? No. You could say we're still in the relationship building stage. By the way, my name is Daniel."

"I'm Lisa."

"Are you sure?"

"Yes," she laughed as the two picked up the final flyers. "Am I right in guessing that as soon as I walk off you will once again be sprinting for your life?"

Daniel looked back at the seniors once again, "That would be a logical conclusion."

"How about we make a deal? I'll walk you to your room, if you agree to come to this meeting at the Christian Student Center in two weeks. "

"Do I have to get saved?"

"No. It's a lesson on relationships. My uncle is the speaker. Not that you need help on relationships," smiled Lisa.

"You've got a deal, but what if they attack anyway? Are you going to help me fight them off?"

"Silly boy, I'm a college girl. I'm carrying enough mace to wipe out half the college."

Chapter 4

ACCEPTANCE

Tuesday – June 19, 1990
1:35 PM
Southern Fork Trail

"SO, my cousin says that here in the near future people will be getting their mail on a computer instead of at the mailbox," shared Alex as he and Will hiked along. They had been together for the last two days.

"A computer? That's crazy. You would need a spare room just to hold one big enough to do something like that. My college had a computer that simply calculated schedules and it took up a two-story building."

Supposedly one day they will have computers you can fit in your hand and will be able to do everything from telephone, camera, even show you a map of your location."

"Maybe so, but who wants to walk around with a telephone line and extension cord hanging on them.

Oh well, I doubt it will be in our lifetime. They'll have flying cars before they'll have computers that fit in your pocket." The two guys slowed as they approached a fork in the trail sprinkled with a medley of odd objects; from hiking sticks to trinkets hanging in trees. As Alex and Will perused their surroundings they noticed an old man taking a nap behind a mound of dirt. "I think we just stumbled into the Christmas tree forest complete with Santa Claus," whispered Will.

They were about to sneak away quietly when the old Rip Van Winkle opened his eyes. "Welcome to the Southern Fork. Which way you boys headed from here?

"That's a bit uncertain," said Will who pulled out his folded map.

"Oh, I see," smiled the old man "You boys are lost?"

"Not lost," replied Alex, who was now perusing the oddities that lined the trail. "Just not sure where we are headed."

"Well, that's easy if you know where you want to go," chuckled the man as he suddenly hopped to his feet, raised a stick and began pointing. "If you go left, that's the easy route. It's all downhill. Nothing much to see. It ends after a half-day journey at a dead end parking lot. From there you can catch a ride into town and your hike is over."

"And if we go right?" asked Will.

"Well that's a whole other story. It leads you on a whole other adventure through mountains, and rivers, swamps and valleys. It will take weeks to reach the end high on Oglethorpe Mountain; that is, if you finish at all."

Will and Alex looked at each other as they waited for the other to speak. Finally Will broke the silence. "If you need to head home, I understand."

"No," replied Alex. "I think I'll stay out here a little longer. You're welcome to join me unless you need to get back. I'm sure your friends are waiting on you."

"No," answered Will. "They're all on their own journeys and anyway, what kind of friend would I be if I left you out here alone. You heard the old man; it's going to get rough. This is no solo journey."

Alex prodded his companion one last time, "You up for such a commitment?"

Will stared back without any doubt in his eyes, "Let's go see this Oglethorpe Mountain."

Relieved, Alex smiled, "After you my friend."

Will took a couple steps when the old man stopped him, "If you're going that way, then these gifts were left for you. It is trail law that people getting off the trail leave a gift for those continuing on. Proper etiquette is for you to choose one."

Alex and Will slowly walked along the trail looking at all the items left behind. In time Will found a tin cased pocket watch buried in a tree notch. He dug it out and popped it open. *The timing is off just a little...*Will adjusted the time and gave it a solid wind. *That's better. It just needed a little help.*

Alex wandered on past Will and finally, while looking high into a tree, saw something that caught his fancy. He climbed branch after branch until he could reach it. When he returned to the ground, he held in his hand a leather band necklace with a wooden cross. His family had once gone to church, and it was a place he dearly missed.

"Looks like you boys have made your decision," said the old man. "May your journey go well." Alex and Will turned to say thank you, but before they could muster such a response the old man was sound asleep.

Monday – September 13, 2010
12:10 PM
Sunrise Youth Development Center

The cafeteria at the Sunrise Youth Development Center had a dull yellow paint that years ago was probably put there to uplift the spirits of its incarcerated guests. Time, neglect, and what appeared to be a thin layer of grease had long diminished its cheerful nature. Still, it was where everyone gathered for sustenance and the possibility of excitement.

Matthew stood in the lunch line trying not to lean on the wall in the process. Out of the three weeks he had been here, today he felt more nervous than ever. It was his hope to simply survive this arena of pressure and make it back to his room, but as the guy behind him nudged him, slipped something in his back pocket and nodded towards a crowded table, reality rudely burst in. The moment he had been dreading was suddenly upon him. Matthew took a deep breath summoning what courage he had and broke out of line. Before he or any of the guards knew it, Matthew was at the packed table standing behind a new kid he knew nothing about; nothing except that this kid was his target. As every eye in the room slowly turned to him, he reached into his back pocket only to withdraw it at the last second. Instead he reared back and sent his fist flying hitting his target in the back of his head. The second shot caught the side of the smaller kids face and drew blood as the corner of his lip popped. There was never going to be a third shot. The next collision was Matthew's body with the cold, hard floor and over 300 pounds of state paid force atop him.

Almost as quickly as Matthew hit the ground, he was jerked up and forcefully escorted out of the cafeteria down a hallway and into a cell. Along the way the guards searched him and took the deadly shank out of his back pocket. With the slam of the door only one thought echoed through Matthew's mind as he collapsed in the corner. *What have I done?*

The room was purposefully small and Matthew had accepted the idea that he would likely be spending days in solitary confinement. He tried to take a nap, but the scene of him attacking someone he didn't even know continued to play over and over in his head. Tears began to well up in his eyes, but he knew he could not allow them to flow, not even now. With his eyes closed, he leaned his head back to fight the gravity. He was huddled in the corner in this odd position for almost an hour when the door swung open. "Mr. Barrow wants to see you," stated the guard.

Wiping what was left of the tears in his eyes, he stood up and walked one step ahead of the guard towards the last place he wanted to go. Along the way, he had to cross the main yard where several of his peers were busy cleaning the grounds or playing ball. They all looked his way, but one in particular flashed a sign to him. Matthew knew very little gang sign, but this one was clear, "Don't be a rat!"

A short rap on the door by the guard was answered, "Come in."

"Matthew Harris is here, as you requested," replied the guard as he escorted him in.

"Thank you. I'll call when we're finished talking." With that the guard moved on leaving Matthew alone with the one man he didn't want to see.

"Have a seat Matthew."

"I won't be a rat!" blurted out Matthew as he dropped into the chair.

"It is apparent you have no idea what you will or will not do," replied the counselor. "Three weeks ago you had no idea you would attack someone just to join the ranks of Mr. Andrews and his gang." Matthew felt a cold chill climb his spine. "Are you surprised I knew that? To be honest, we've known this would be a possibility since the moment you arrived. My job is to help you understand why you did it."

"I don't know what you're talking about," puffed Matthew. "I hit that punk because I didn't like the way he was staring at me."

"Number one, if you got upset when people looked at you wrong you would be in 300 fights a day. Number two, Benjamin, the kid you attacked, never laid eyes on you. You hit him from behind. And, number three," stated Mr. Barrow as he pulled out the sharpened instrument placed in Matthew's pocket just before the fight,

"If you were truly the angry mongrel that you claim to be, this would be covered in blood right now." At the sight of the shank Matthew froze. "Let's try this again, why did you attack Benjamin in the cafeteria?"

"I did it to join the gang," blurted out Matthew with such emotion it shocked him.

"And why do you need to join a gang?" prodded Mr. Barrow.

"I have no friends here. I need…"

"Acceptance?" asked the counselor.

"Yes."

"Now we're getting somewhere."

Tuesday – September 14, 2010
4:10 PM
Big State University

It was a cloudy Tuesday afternoon and the corner of Eighth and Jefferson was the loneliest place on campus. Far from any major buildings the abandoned bench that rested here under a tree was Rose's favorite location to receive phone calls. Besides there being no interruptions and therefore lots of privacy, the corner had great reception. Rose looked at the time on her phone and then glanced at her watch to double check it. *It's ten after four, little brother. You said you would call at four.* Five more minutes passed when suddenly her phone began to vibrate. "Hello."

"Hey sis. How are things going?"

"I'm good, but you're late?"

"Sorry about that. I'm still learning how things work

here. Apparently four is when I can begin standing in line for a phone. Please forgive me."

"You're forgiven. How did your week go?"

"Fine, I guess...I mean I did get in a fight yesterday."

"I told you no fighting Benjamin Hawkins! You may not remember, but we were raised better than that!"

"Relax Rose. I didn't instigate it or finish it for that matter. I don't even know who it was, or what I did to provoke him."

"Are you okay?"

"Just a busted lip. No big deal."

"Well, lay low and work your program. I need you back out here soon."

"I'll see you as soon as I can. Listen, I've got to go. Take care of yourself."

"You too, bro."

As the phone call ended, Rose noticed the wind pick up bringing the dark clouds above ever so closer. Tossing her knapsack over her shoulder she hurried down the road along a route few other college students ever traveled. Far from the crisp landscape of academia she walked along the outer limits of an old manufacturing plant before turning down an old alley into a neighborhood that had not seen its glory days in decades. There, in the midst of cracking old houses filled with cracking old people, Rose walked into a home that from the outside appeared to be the poorest of them all.

"Hey Rose!" greeted a small girl in a wheelchair.

"Hello Amelia. Where is the rest of the gang?"

"John is in the living room reading. Hey John, Rose is here!"

Almost immediately, a young boy carrying a Braille book walked up. "I'm sorry. I didn't see you come in," laughed John.

Rose gave him a big hug. "And where is Jenny?"

"Nurse Ratched took her to the doctor to adjust her leg braces."

"Nurse Ratched? I should have never let you watch that movie!" laughed Rose through the scarf on her face.

"Why do you wear that scarf on your face?" asked Amelia. "It's pretty, but not as pretty as you."

With a tear in her eye Rose took the scarf off to reveal a terrible scar running across her cheek and down her chin. "Not everyone is as understanding as you guys." She took the scarf, folded it once and put it in her back pocket. "Let's go make some snacks. I'm starved!"

Sunday – September 26, 2010
6:58 PM
Christian Student Center
at Big State University

It had been weeks since Caleb's one and only visit to the Christian Student Center. He had told himself he would never return, yet here he was on a Sunday night about to enter the front door. *This is not a social event, it's purely academia. I'm not here to make friends. I'm just here to pick up a bulletin so I can have proof I attended this speaker and get extra-credit in class.*

"Greetings Caleb. My name is Mr. George. I'm glad you could come." The campus minister shook his hand and handed him a brochure. Caleb nodded and smiled back, slightly puzzled that Mr. George knew his name, but in too much of a rush to inquire. He had come at the brink of being late, in the hopes of not having to run into many people, and for the most part it worked. Only one smiling girl now stood in the foyer.

"Hello. Thanks for coming. My name is Lisa."

"I'm Caleb. Did no one else show up?"

"Everyone is already seated. Would you like to sit with me? I have someone I would like to introduce you to."

Caleb didn't know quite how to react. He had come in with his defenses up expecting quite the opposite reception. Looking him in the eyes, Lisa gently reached out and softly tapped his forearm. "I won't bite. I promise."

With a quiet laugh Caleb did a slight bow, "After you." Lisa led him down the hall and into the main auditorium where a large crowd of people sat quietly talking while waiting on the lecture to start. As he perused the audience, suddenly he noticed a familiar face look back at him and then begin waving. Lisa headed straight for him.

"Caleb this is ..."

"Daniel," Caleb replied as the two shook hands.

"Oh good, you two have met."

"That, we have," smiled Daniel. "Have a seat, my friend."

"And save my seat," interjected Lisa. "I'll be back in just a moment."

It wasn't long before the quiet conversation ceased and Mr. George took the stage. "Welcome, friends. Let me start by thanking you all for coming and reassuring you that I am not the speaker tonight. That job falls to an old friend who I first met on a journey long ago. I would introduce him, but I'm even giving that job away to his niece. Now, I do have one job tonight. I know our audience is a mix of CSC regulars and several visitors from campus. This is targeted towards those of you who want to be a core part of our ministry here. In the following weeks, we will be hosting a teambuilding workshop provided by Challenge Point. I'm hoping to build a team of students who not only dream of a better ministry, but are willing to work for it. Now, concerning tonight, this is the first of a two-part series. The second part takes place during our Fall Retreat next month. I hope to see you all there. Miss Hastings, the stage is yours."

At that point Mr. George sat down and to everyone's surprise up walked Lisa. "Christianity is not a solo journey. We were created to be connected. Those were two statements my uncle shared with me several times while growing up. I wish I had listened to him more. I came here last year and just expected that I would make friends for life. Unfortunately, I was also afraid to step out of the shadows and do the work that is required to make good friends. I was in fear that if I stepped out and let down my defenses, I would get hurt. Well, I got hurt anyway and didn't have true friends to fall back on. I'm working hard now to make sure that never happens. Well, enough about me. May I introduce my uncle, Mr. Barrow."

The audience gave a polite round of applause while Mr. Barrow took the stage and gave his niece a hug. He took a moment to capture the listeners with his eyes, then smiled, "As my niece has pointed out, we were all created to be connected." And from there he continued on...

Chapter 5

THE FIRST
FIVE STAGES

Relationships

WE are created for relationships. Everyone has them. Some you want. Some you don't. Some are brief and some last a lifetime. Some are simple and some are intimately complex. Some fill you with joy and some drain your energy to the bone. Some you would give your life for, and for some you may have contemplated taking a life to end it. Whatever the case, relationships are an intricate part of our lives.

As a child, I listed my relationships from best to worst, as if they each had a score – The hot red-head in kindergarten was my best friend. Cousin Jerry was my second best friend, until he said his dog was smarter than mine. Then he became my arch nemesis. The boy I rode ponies with was my third best friend. As an adult though, I realize relationships are too complex, too fluid, simply to label and place in a box on a shelf. Just like us, relationships live and grow. They react to good times and bad times. At times they are healthy, and at times they struggle. Fact is, they are continuously developing.

Relationships exist in different growth stages – different levels of depth, and throughout a relationship's existence, it may progress and digress through all stages. And, that my friends, is what we are going to be looking at. During this time we are going to look at eight stages of development and examine the characteristics of relationships in each stage. Many of you here are Christians, so we will view the Christian perspective, but we will also look at it from a leadership viewpoint.

To start things off I'm going to define relationships in the most simplified manner possible. Relationships are a series of encounters between two individuals, each one building off the last. Those encounters are direct (face to face) and indirect (email, phone, text, etc...) At each encounter we exchange information, services, goods, and emotions.

- **Information** – One of the first relationships you ever had was with your parents or caregiver. They fed and clothed you (goods), washed and changed you (service), gave you hugs and kisses (emotion), and taught you the basics of life (information). From there hopefully you became a sponge for knowledge. You soaked in data and lessons from siblings (this is how you perform a wedgie), relatives (do not pull Uncle Bob's finger), teachers (history, math and language), and ministers (God loves you). In adulthood you continue to do the same thing, whether it is through a mentoring relationship, reading your favorite journalist's article or blog, sitting at the table with family and learning how their day went, or asking your closest friend advice on a pressing issue in your life.

- **Services and Goods** – You may be able to count all your family and friends on one hand, but I guarantee you have more relationships than that. The lady at the post office, the cashier at the mini-market down the road, the girl who always sells you cookies in the spring, the college-kid at the nursery who always helps with the plants and bags of soil – you have a relationship with all these people. It may not be deep, but it is a relationship nonetheless. Of course, services and goods are exchanged in stronger relationships as well. If you break down on the side of the road, do you know who you would call for help? Hopefully we all have that close friend or relative that always has our back.

- **Emotions** – Ever been on an adventure by yourself and wish you had someone to experience it with? That's what friends are for. When you get mad, excited, or are overjoyed, I'm guessing you share it with a friend. Emotions, like experiences are best shared with others. It is how we get rid of stress and unload our burden. It's how we get inspired to pursue our dreams. Without relationships, we would be so boring we would explode into dust, or so psychotically mad we would be serial killers. Truth is, friendship gets us through our bad times and is essential for the good times.

A Two Way Road

We all know that it takes two to form and grow a relationship. It is a give and take process. Like dancing, even if one of you is really good at it, if the other is lame, you're probably not winning any trophies anytime soon.

During this time, we are going to look at what you put into the relationship and how you deal with the other individual's input. Still, no matter what great advice we give and no matter what you do with it, you must have the right person on the other end for the relationship to go deeper. That is the nature of relationships.

Acknowledgement

Every series of encounters must first start with that initial encounter. It is the moment of acknowledgement. The first time your paths cross and you are face to face with a person, mutually aware that the two of you exist, acknowledgement has occurred and a relationship has begun. What happens beyond that point depends on the needs of the individuals, and how they treat one another.

There are three routes the relationship will take from that initial encounter: Acceptance, Apathy or Abhorrence. All three go in extremely different directions with exceptionally different results. If you happen to head down one direction and decide later to take the relationship down a different path, it can be extraordinarily costly in time and effort. That's why making smart decisions at the point of Acknowledgement is so important. Let's look at these three routes.

Apathy — "I truly don't care about you. Your existence means nothing to me."

If you were to add up all of the relationships in the world, the majority would land in this category. It is the realm of no concern or interest. It requires no feelings, emotions, energy, or sacrifice.

The journey from Acknowledgement to Apathy

The path from Acknowledgement to Apathy is simple. All it requires is an emotionless or disinterested response. Nonverbally it's a stare without a smile, a flippant glance, or no eye contact at all. It's crossing your arms and looking away, or turning your back in the midst of their conversation. Verbally it's "I don't care." "Why are you still here?" "Whatever."

Often we don't intentionally place our relationships in this category. Unfortunately without effort and discipline, relationships easily fall into this chasm. Depending on how busy your life is, you may start a new relationship weekly, daily, or several in a day. Most are those brief moments when we meet people to exchange goods, services or knowledge. Often, since there is no evident emotional benefit, we don't invest any emotion into the transaction, and just like that, we unintentionally toss a relationship into Apathy.

Still, some people are notorious for placing their everyday relationships in this pit. These people are often 'users' – those that mistreat people until they need something from them. If you were ever in high school and felt snubbed by an individual until they needed your homework, then you know first hand what I'm talking about.

Influence

Influence is the power of affecting people. Every relationship, even the brief ones, creates an emotional reaction and therefore has a touch of influence on those involved. For every apathetic relationship you have, you are telling that person, "You don't matter." Now the closer you are bonded to a person, the stronger your influence is on that individual. Apathetic relationships are generally not highly influential, except for those that had a prior history of deeper connection. Still, even the brief ones have a small impact nonetheless. Every encounter is like placing a tiny nail in their coffin. It's small, but it does exist.

The Christian Perspective

As Christians we are called to represent Christ on this earth. During Jesus' time here, He treated everyone like they were of great value. He created us and knows our true potential. He was willing to die for all of us (John 3:16). In His eyes there were no lower-class individuals who didn't matter. Everyone mattered. He even shook the social classes when he stated in Luke 9:48, "For he who is least among you all – he is the greatest."

One command spoken by Christ should be taken into consideration every time we decide to place a relationship into the category of Apathy. Matthew 7:1-2 – "Do not judge, or you too will be judged. For in the same way you judge others, you will be judged, and with the measure you use, it will be measured to you". The last thing I would want to hear from my Creator is, "You mean nothing to me. I truly don't care about you."

The Leadership Perspective

If you want me to follow you, before you impress me with your sterling character and passionately share with me your vision of how things can be greater, you must first show me that you care about me. I need to know that you have my best interest at heart. I need to know that you value who I am.

It's that simple. The first thing a leader needs to learn is how to treat individuals as if they matter. That's how you build influence, and as John Maxwell says, "The true measure of leadership is influence - nothing more, nothing less." If you decide to place yourself on a pedestal and look apathetically down on others, you will soon be standing by yourself.

Abhorrence – "I utterly hate and despise you."

In the fictional world, most every character has an arch nemesis. Batman has the Joker, Peter Pan has Captain Hook, and Barbie has that trollop who is dating Ken. In the real world Republicans have Democrats, Jews have radical Muslims, Christians have atheists, and the entire world has neo-Nazis. Our social world is built around contrasting views and opinions. Such conflicting values can breed relationships that exist in the realm of Abhorrence. It is where I not only don't care about you, but I utterly hate and despise everything about you. I truly want the flames of Hell to consume you and torture your soul for eternity. Now, you may think that is a little harsh, but this is where relationships enveloped in hatred exist, and I'm not good at differentiating the separate degrees of hatred. Hate is hate.

Don't confuse hate for dislike though. There are people in this world whom you may dislike. Due to their history and opinions you may hate everything they stand for, but you still value the individual. The chemistry of your personalities may be so conflicting that you may dread being in their presence, and if given the choice, you may do everything you can to dodge them. The difference is, at night as you lie in bed, you don't dream of their death and destruction. You may feel sorry for the person, and celebrate the idea of them moving to another continent, but you're not at the point where you draw great joy from their pain and misery.

Like and dislike is a feeling, and sometimes, no matter how hard we try, we cannot control our feelings. Hate is an effort fueled by a mindset. It is something that consumes the heart and requires a great amount of energy. It is a choice. We can change the mindset and starve the flames.

The journey from Acknowledgement to Abhorrence

I would like to think that rarely do individuals meet and immediately hate one another. Dislike – yes, but not hate. One exception would be individuals with strong ideological beliefs who meet their opposite on the ideological spectrum and allow their disagreement to consume that relationship. People who have a built-in hatred for another race, sex, idea, belief, or lifestyle would fall into this category.

Generally a relationship falls into Abhorrence after a history has been established and someone has been hurt. Often it is those who have grown close, and then the relationship goes terribly bad, leaving pain and sorrow to fuel the hatred. Sometimes it's due to extreme jealousy or the feeling of being back-stabbed. You put your trust in someone and that person did you wrong. He lied and cheated you. She hurt you, and that hurt festered into hatred.

Influence

A relationship in Abhorrence does have influence, but not the type either individual would hope to wield. In war opposing parties win only after crippling the other side and forcing their surrender. Never has a war ended when both parties were even and one side suddenly said, "Oh, I understand your viewpoint now and I completely agree with you." The same thing is true when individuals hate one another. Abhorrent relationships simply become more polarized and the source of the hatred grows. You will never win your enemies over and change them by hating them.

The Christian Perspective

Throughout the history of mankind, terrible atrocities have been done in the name of Christianity, which were clearly fueled by one man's hatred for the next. In all my studies of the Bible, I have yet to find where God, Who is love, wants me to hate an individual. Disagree with them – yes, but not hate.

In contrast, there are several scriptures that warn against hatred. Here are my favorites: I John 4:8, 20 – "Whoever does not love, does not know God, because God is love. If anyone says I love God, yet hates his brother, he is a liar. For anyone who does not love his brother, whom he has seen, cannot love God, whom he has not seen."

In Proverbs we are given examples of behaviors God hates. I believe these are all fruits of our own hatred. Proverbs 6:16-19 – "There are six things the Lord hates, seven that are detestable to Him: haughty eyes, a lying tongue, hands that shed innocent blood, a heart that devises wicked schemes, feet that are quick to rush to evil, a false witness that pours out lies, and a man who stirs up dissension among brothers."

In the big picture, I believe if we have relationships in Abhorrence that is robbing us of the joy we should be experiencing in our relationship with God and with others. As I said before, hatred consumes us, taking time and energy. It eats into our heart and spirit. It chains us down and keeps us from moving forward in our Christian journey. I know of no one who is worth that.

The Leadership Perspective

Leaders set the standard. They are a magnet for followers, who want to take the journey with you and often emulate your character along the way. Unless hatred for people is part of the dream you are selling, (Hitler comes to mind) it has no place in your life.

Leadership carries with it enough burdens. You will likely have people who dislike what you stand for, and who dislike you as a person. Conflict is an inevitable part of working with people. If you succumb to hatred though, it will consume you, your reaction to those you lead, and your vision. Hatred is a stumbling block for leaders and if left unchecked, it will cause their ultimate downfall.

Alcatraz (Quarantine)

We are all human and sometimes the chemistry between two people can be so bad that they need to stay away from each other at all cost. I'm not referring to something petty, like two squabbling teens who have clashing bad attitudes. No, I'm thinking about the darker side.

There are horrible crimes and terrible situations that leave people deeply injured and sometimes scarred. Divorce, physical abuse, sexual abuse, emotional abuse, addictions, murder... the list could go on. The relationships that brought about or were involved in such destruction are often so toxic that it does nothing but harm to those involved. In relationships where one person has a strong and destructive influence over another, to keep them together is nothing short of criminal.

The bottom line is some relationships are dangerous and for the sake of those involved, those relationships should be placed in quarantine. This detention may last briefly while people heal and are able to come back

together and resolve their problems. Some relationships may need to be quarantined indefinitely. The key
is Quarantine is better than Abhorrence. Time usually
heals, but not when consumed with hate.

Acceptance - *"I value you as an individual, no matter what."*

Everyone wants to be accepted. Everyone wants to
be valued as an individual. Even the most independent
spirits want to feel as if they belong to something bigger
than just themselves. From our very creation it has been
placed in the heart of who we are. We were created to be
connected.

Placing a relationship into the realm of Acceptance
basically means you will treat that person with the
mindset that she is a human being worthy of basic
respect. It is treating her like she matters and like you
honestly care about her. It is entering the relationship
in peace and without any agenda or standards that the
other must meet just to get a smile out of you. It is a
neutral zone where each individual is treated with basic
goodness.

Acceptance doesn't mandate that you agree with the
person or even that you like him. You may be mortal
enemies in the political field or totally disagree on some
social agenda. This person may have a history you find
appalling or a lifestyle you completely disagree with
down to the core of your being. Acceptance is where you
put that aside and focus on the sole individual. You over-
look your clashing personalities and take the high road.
You appreciate the person as a fellow human being.

Acceptance is not something he has to earn, it is something given freely.

The journey from
Acknowledgement to Acceptance

Acceptance is a mindset one has to have before the moment of Acknowledgement even occurs. It needs to become a part of your character. Long before you decide whether you like this person or not, you must make the decision that this person is a valued fellow man and therefore worthy of basic respect. Once again, this is a mindset and a choice, not a feeling.

At the point of Acknowledgement, the path to Acceptance begins with what our grandparents called common decency. It's looking someone in the eye and greeting her with a smile. It's calling her by her name. It's using your manners like yes sir, no ma'am, excuse me, please, thank you, and you're welcome. It's shaking a hand or giving a pat on the back. It's holding a door for her or providing unrequested assistance. It's paying attention to her conversation. It is simply treating the person with common respect.

Influence

Acceptance is where the first signs of positive influence occur. It has the ability to change a person's heart. It may only be a small touch of influence, but it is more powerful than a relationship in Apathy or Abhorrence. For brief relationships, it may only serve to lift his spirit for the day or build his trust in mankind as a whole. For relationships that will have a longer lifespan, it is laying the groundwork for that bond to grow deeper.

The Christian Perspective

As Christians, we are called to love our fellow man. Once again, let me share some of my favorite scripture: I John 4:7, 9, 10, 19 – "Dear friends, let us love one another, for love comes from God. This is how God showed His love among us: He sent His one and only Son into the world that we might live through Him. This is love: not that we loved God, but that He loved us and sent His Son as an atoning sacrifice for our sins. We love because He first loved us."

Jesus Himself even commanded us to love our enemies: Matthew 5:43, 44 – "You have heard that it was said, 'Love your neighbor and hate your enemy.' But I tell you: Love your enemies and pray for those who persecute you, that you may be sons of your Father in heaven."

What is this love that we are commanded to bestow upon our enemies? What are its characteristics? I Corinthians 13:4-7 – "Love is patient, love is kind, it does not envy, it does not boast, it is not proud. It is not easily angered; it keeps no record of wrongs. Love does not delight in evil, but rejoices with the truth. It always protects, always trusts, always hopes, always perseveres."

Nowhere in the Bible does it say we have to 'like' people, but it is flooded with the commandment to love people. It is treating people as if they are a valuable creation of God. It is being patient and kind and good to individuals, no matter if they deserve it or not.

As a Christian, the number of relationships we should have in the realm of Acceptance is 100%. It is all of them. We are not called to hate or to be apathetic. We are called to love.

When people visit your church, your campus or teen ministry, they want to be accepted. They don't need to be given a set of righteous rules they must meet first, or any social requirements. They need unconditional acceptance, and that is what our Lord asks us to give. God showed us unconditional love, and that should be the first thing we shower on them. We all have a lifetime to become more Christ-like.

Do you disagree with someone's teachings? Meet on a common ground of respect before you try to change his mind. Do you disagree with someone's lifestyle? Don't run from him. Treat him with love. You cannot impact a person unless you first take time to build influence.

The Leadership Perspective

I'll say it again, because it is worth repeating. If you want me to follow you, you must first show me that you care about me. I need to know you are aware of my value as a person. As a leader, one of your missions is to build influence among your people. You cannot do that from a pedestal. You cannot walk around and ignore people in your group. You cannot stick to a particular clique and expect their popularity to win you followers. Demonstrating your leadership by initiating relationships is part of your calling.

In comparison to Apathy and Abhorrence, the best thing about Acceptance is it's not a dead end road. On this fertile ground, relationships can continue to grow and blossom. From Acceptance we mature into Affirmation.

Affirmation - "Through my words and actions, I will build you up and not tear you down."

One of the biggest fears of forming relationships is rejection - to make yourself available and then to be turned down. That's why Acceptance is so important. Equal to that, is the fear of your friends discovering your faults and using them to destroy you. It is the reason many people settle for shallow superficial relationships. There is safety in hiding behind a polished persona.

Taking a relationship to the level of Affirmation succumbs such fear. Here there is an understanding that I will build you up and not tear you down. I have your best interest at heart, and I am not out to hurt you. Through my words and actions, I will encourage and support you. I'm not interested in defeating you.

Once again, this is an intentional effort of those involved and works best when both parties share in this agreement. Of course, relationships are not like business deals where all the terms are laid out and agreed upon at the beginning. In every relationship you can control what you bring to the table and nothing else. The good news is, if you build the discipline needed for Affirmation relationships, it tends to be contagious.

From Acceptance to Affirmation

For brief relationships where encounters are few and far between, Acceptance is enough. But, for those relationships where encounters are common, Affirmation adds a touch of depth and gives you a bit more influence. It is an intentional effort of providing a compliment at every encounter. If the relationship is new, it may be as simple as complimenting a lady's shoes (Be careful not to be cheesy). For relationships where you know more about the person, it's pointing out some quality of her character or work that you truly appreciate. Sincerity is of the utmost importance.

I've always been told that women appreciate compliments when they are expressed in an emotion. For example, "I like when you..." or "It makes me happy to see you..." Men, on the other hand will give you their full attention when you point out something that you respect about them. "I really respect how you...." I do know for a fact that our ears perk up and our chests pop out when we hear the word respect connected with our name.

Take note that relationships can and should exist in the realm of Affirmation even if you don't like the other person. It may be difficult to encourage him. It may require you to rack your brain and find that one characteristic about him that you don't find vile and then point it out to him. The good news is he will likely take note of that one good quality and exercise it around you at the next encounter. Positive reinforcement can grow a seed in the poorest soil.

Affirmation also means I will not do anything to hurt

you. I will not talk bad about you to your face, and I will not speak poorly of you behind your back. The only gossip I will spread about you is that which shines a light on your good character and accomplishments.

There is a place for constructive criticism, just as there is an art to pointing out flaws where it does no damage to the relationship. For every critique, there needs to be just as much encouragement on what is working right, As Mary Poppins says, "A spoon full of sugar helps the medicine go down." Of course, at this stage, I would only provide constructive criticism if it was absolutely necessary. I would increase my influence in the relationship before I went down that road.

Influence

People appreciate a sincere compliment, even if it comes from someone they dislike. Kind words always make an impact, whether you are able to see it or not. Even more important is what you don't say. If I know you will not say a bad word towards me, even behind my back, I am much more likely to trust you.

This is an excellent stage for building influence and possibly advancing the relationship; however, at this stage building influence is a work in progress. Don't be surprised if you cannot sway a person with a few kind words.

The Christian Perspective

In the same way that loving people is commanded by God, encouraging one another is apparently rather important to God as well. I Thessalonians 5:11 – "Therefore

encourage one another and build each other up..."
Ephesians 4:29 – "Do not let any unwholesome talk
come out of your mouths, but only what is helpful for
building others up according to their needs, that it may
benefit those who listen." The word encourage and edify
is throughout the Bible. There is a reason why "Love
your neighbor" is the second command only behind
"Love the Lord." It is our mission to encourage and
build each other up.

It doesn't only apply to fellow Christians though.
Jesus commanded us in Luke 6:27 – "Love your enemies,
do good to those who hate you, bless those who curse
you, pray for those who mistreat you." It is easy to bless
those who bless you, but when they are cursing you,
blessing others becomes a true test of your character.

There is nothing easy about growing relationships in
the Affirmation level, but as a Christian we should aspire
to have all our relationships here – 100%. Every relationship we have is an opportunity to bring someone to
Christ. This is where the work comes in. They will likely
not be impressed if you throw scripture at them or pray
and fast in front of them. What does make an impact is
how you treat them. Can you treat them better than the
non-believer? Can you do so without them deserving it?
Can you make them curious about why you would do
such a thing?

The Leadership Perspective

Developing leadership is all about the little steps. It
is growing one relationship at a time. It is being consis-
tent with your character at every encounter in those

relationships. If you give me encouragement during my encounter with you, I'm going to seek you out for a future encounter. If I believe you see me as valuable, I'm going to trust you with something small. If I learn that you kept my confidence and didn't use what I shared with you to hurt me, I'm going to trust you with something bigger. If you handle that well, you have my complete trust and I'm going to follow you.

No one should expect full trust just through declaring oneself trustworthy. A leader is tested one step at a time, one encounter at a time. Developing relationships in which people know that you are going to build them up and not tear them down is essential to having their trust.

Chapter 6

AFFIRMATION

Tuesday – June 26, 1990
_4:32 PM_
Southern Fork Trail

"IS this mountain ever going to end?" shouted Alex as he and Will marched upward. The two had scaled three mountains that day and had brazenly taken on a fourth even though the sun was close to setting. The old man at the fork had not lied when he warned that this route would be tougher. The last five days had kicked his tail.

"I think I see the top!" Will replied as he used his makeshift staff to pull himself ever upward. "Of course, this is the third time I thought I saw the summit." The two hiked on and the top soon showed itself to merely be a hump in the ever rising horizon. The trail curved around the mountain and disappeared along a shallow ridgeline. Will, who was up ahead made his way over the rocky cleft until he was out of sight from Alex. Seeing his moment, Alex stopped and dropped his pack. He reached into the top pocket and pulled out a prescription bottle of little round pills. He didn't know what they were. He didn't care. Around two months ago he had found them in his mother's purse and had started taking them. They helped the pain go away. Mental, emotional, physical – it all went away with the pop of a precious pill.

He grabbed his water, downed one, and then sat there with his eyes closed waiting for the magic to occur. It was at this moment that Will yelled, "Are you okay?" It startled Alex and he jumped up in a panic. "I'm good! I'm coming!" He turned around quickly to gather his stuff, when in his haste he knocked over his bottle of pills. They hit the rock below, and bounced off three more rocks before making their final flight off the ledge. Alex jumped down on his knees only to see the brown bottle disappear into the tree cover below.

The rest of the hike was a haze for Alex. Not because of the one pill he took, but because of the fear that set in over the pills he had lost. *Can I keep going without the pills? How can I get some more? Will there be any in the next town? I wonder if Will can deal with the real me?*

That night the two once again sat around a campfire eating their late dinners. "It was a rough day today," shared Will.

"Yes, it was," replied Alex.

"But we made it, and no worse for wear. It's still better than the best day in the office."

"Will, can I ask you something?"

"Ask away, my friend"

"Have I been a good hiking companion?"

The question didn't seem to rattle Will a bit. "You've been an excellent hiking companion. Why do you ask?"

"Well, things might get rough in the coming days and I might not be as pleasant to be around."

"I don't want to sound like we are married, but when we made our decision at the fork, I figured I would be sticking with you through thick and thin. I wasn't expecting this to be cotton candy and unicorn rides."

"So if I get grumpy?"

"Then I will hike with a grumpy Alex." Will could tell something deeper was bothering Alex, but he didn't want to come out and ask directly. Still, he felt he needed to reassure him of his commitment. "Listen, this is my pledge to you. At any point you can go off and make this your solo journey, but if you stick with me I'll do everything I can to build you up and never tear you down. I only want the best for you on this journey."

Alex's natural inclination was to say "Ditto," or "Back at you," but he stopped himself. He didn't trust himself with such a promise. Instead he settled for a simple "Thank you."

That night, as he curled up in his sleeping bag, he cried his first tear of the trip. Not because of the wave of pain from his parent's divorce. That would hit him much later. Tonight he cried because he knew he was about to kill a friendship.

Friday – September 24, 2010
4:12 PM
Sunrise Youth Development Center

For the first time in several days Matthew stepped out into the courtyard with the general population and stared up at the sun. Since his little escapade in the cafeteria, he had been on a tight leash. Besides having more contemplative time in his room, his counseling sessions had increased to the point he couldn't decide if he loved Mr. Barrow, or absolutely hated him. At this very moment the feeling was closer to irritation, but he knew if his project went well, that may subside.

Across the yard near one of the basketball goals stood Benjamin nonchalantly bouncing a ball and occasionally attempting a shot. Though the courtyard was crowded, he was alone. After two weeks, he had made no connections with the other inmates. He was smaller than most and after receiving his beat down from Matthew others saw him as weak. The last several days had been rough as he endured others picking on him. Even now he was merely waiting for his next assault.

Matthew walked over to the boundary of the court and waited for his moment. When Benjamin tossed the ball at the hoop and it bounced to the side Matthew took advantage of the opportunity and retrieved it. The moment Benjamin saw him his whole body tightened up and his hands rolled into fists. "Are you here to finish the job?"

Matthew tossed the ball to him. "I'm here to say I'm sorry. I had no reason to attack you."

"Then why did you do it?"

"I'm stupid."

"Well, evidently we all are, or else we wouldn't be here in this void of despair. Any more differentiating justification?"

Matthew paused for a moment, "You mean any other excuses? That's an impressive vocabulary you have on you. I bet you are really smart."

"As I stated before, no I'm not. How about you go find someone else to annoy." And with that, Benjamin turned his back to Matthew and dribbled away from him.

Not knowing what to do Matthew blurted out, "I attacked you because I wanted to join a gang! They told me to do it!"

Benjamin stopped and turned back towards him, "You wanted to join a gang?"

"Well, not really. I just wanted to belong to something bigger than me...I wanted to feel protected. I'm not as brave as you are."

"So now I'm smart and I'm brave? For someone who doesn't know me you sure have a high regard for me. What new game are you playing?"

"No game. I just wanted to apologize and make things right between us. In regards to you being smart and brave, well, I don't know why you are here, but you don't strike me as a thug. I'm not saying you're completely innocuous, but in this lugubrious setting you might be one illuminating point."

"Nice vocabulary," replied Benjamin as he fought back a smile. "I'll accept your apology, but don't get upset if I don't invite you over to spend the night."

"Agreed. Can we shake on it?"

Benjamin got nervous as he looked around. "If you shake hands with me, you will become a target of every gang out here."

Matthew took a deep breath as he also looked around at the crowds watching them. "I'm willing to take that risk." And with that said, he extended his hand and Benjamin grasped it.

Monday – October 4, 2010
8:45 am
Big State University

Andrea stood out in the hall waiting for the last student to walk out of whatever class it was that met before her Psychology class. For the last couple weeks this had become her routine. It was not because of a sudden surge in her academic studiousness. For her, this was a brief escape.

With the room now empty, she walked in and took her regular back seat. It was where she typically sat to watch the parade of freaks march by. But now, it was where she simply rested her head and wrestled with the turmoil within. Her parents had separated early this past summer and filed for divorce. Her father had cheated on her mother, and not just once. Truth be told, it was an adulterous scandal that involved several social circles, including the country club, from which her family had just recently been disgracefully ejected. For several weeks it had all been kept out of the spotlight, but two weeks ago it had all hit the social fan right at the same time her father lost his prestigious job. He had not only been cheating on her mother, he had been cheating the company. Most figured after the courts got through with him he would be spending several years in prison.

While Andrea sat with her head down, the girls who had once worshipped her now walked by without saying a word and sat across the room from her. Though she couldn't hear it, she knew they were talking about her.

As the classroom filled, Andrea sat up just in time to see Rose rush in and then pause looking for a place to sit. Rose knew there was a seat available by Andrea, but she perused the room in hopes of an alternative. When she couldn't find one, she reluctantly took the open seat. "I don't bite," said Andrea with as much nicety as she could muster.

Rose glanced at her, "I'm not worried about your teeth. I just don't want to hear your bark."

"Don't worry. I'm tired of barking…By the way I like your scarf today. It goes well with your blouse. You know, they say paisley plum is the new black."

Rose didn't know how to respond, so she opted to turn her head and ignore the odd compliment. Class soon started and Rose managed to escape any more conversation. When it ended she made a quick departure and was almost out of the building when she came to a sudden halt at the door. Rain poured from the sky.

"Do you need a ride?" asked Andrea as she walked up. "I have a car in the parking deck. We can get there without ever getting wet."

"What is your deal? First you make fun of me and

now suddenly want to be nice to me? Is this some type of game for you?"

"I just wanted to help," replied Andrea.

"Well I'm not your charity case!" exclaimed Rose. And with that, she stomped out into the rain.

Andrea stood there for a second dumfounded and then threw her hands up in the air, "Whatever!" Not wanting to go home and having no friends she could hang out with, several minutes later she found herself crashed on a couch at the Christian Student Center. She had just gotten comfortable wallowing in her own self pity when she was interrupted.

"Andrea, are you okay?"

Andrea pulled the pillow from over her face to see Lisa standing there. "Not you. Not today. I can't deal with it."

"I'm not here to pick a fight with you. To be honest, I'm over the whole Rick saga. I just wanted to know if you are okay. You look down."

Andrea let out a big sigh and then sat up. "Your uncle was wrong. This whole affirmation stage and encouraging people is a load of croc. I just got yelled at for trying to be nice to someone."

"Well, in my uncle's defense he did point out that some people who are hurt do not know how to take encouragement mainly due to mistrust and will often lash out in anger."

"Whatever… So how are you and Rick doing?"

"There is no Rick and I, there never was. He was being nice to me because Mr. George asked him to pull me closer into the fold. That's it. In the end the whole debacle chased him off. No one here has seen him in weeks."

"Oh well. He would have left me by now anyway, just like everyone else. That's all I need is another enemy."

It was now Lisa's turn to take a deep breath. "Andrea, it's evident that we will likely never be best friends, but I do believe we can agree to not be enemies. I can promise you that no matter how difficult it may be, I will not do anything to hurt you or do damage to your reputation."

"I would like that," smiled Andrea as she raised her arm and extended her pinkie. "Pinkie swear?"

Lisa smiled and hooked pinkies with her. "Pinkie swear."

Andrea's smile slowly collapsed into a pitiful grin. "Sadly, you may have just become my closest friend."

Thursday – October 14, 2010
3:02 PM
The Track at Big State University

Daniel had been on the team for just over a month and already he felt like he had been around the track a million times. Today it looked like the coach wanted a million more before practice was over. The team had been given a series of distances along with the times in which they needed to be accomplished. No one on the team was happy. Of course, this was not a generally happy team anyway. It was divided.

Daniel had recently learned there were a limited number of scholarships on the team and the coach used them as incentive. Each semester the coach had the ability to give the scholarships to the fastest on the team. The varsity guys who had them right now were a sour bunch and planned to do everything they could to chase off the competition, hence the toxic atmosphere around the team. As it stood now, it was an unwritten rule that no one passes the seniors during the runs. The newbies always ran in the back.

Today's practice started off as usual with a long period of stretches followed by a warm up run that ended at the track. The coach was there with his stop watch ready to get things going. To everyone's surprise there also stood Caleb, no longer in the stands, but right next to the coach. Daniel anticipated the coach introducing Caleb to the team, but it never happened. Instead Caleb jogged over to the 200 meter mark on the track while the coach lined the team up, "This is your first 400 of the day. I expect you back here in 60 seconds. Caleb will be telling you your 200 times so you can make sure you are on pace."

Daniel was still confused as to Caleb's presence, but when the coach yelled go, he took off in his usual position on the team, which was ahead of the other newbies, but just off the heels of the slowest varsity runner. At the 200 meter mark he became even more confused as Caleb began yelling out times. "Twenty-eight, twenty-nine, thirty, good job varsity! Keep up that pace! Thirty two, Daniel! Pick it up! Thirty-four, thirty five, come on Max! You're faster than that!"

The varsity team continued to run at the same pace so that they crossed right on time, leaving Daniel and the rest to cross the line at 62, 63 and 64 seconds. The coach was furious! "Is this the best you've got! This is what I should expect for the rest of the day? For the rest of the season?" The coach continued to rant as the team took a short breather before the next sprint. As he ranted, Caleb was quietly heard in the background as he walked to each runner and spoke with them.

"You looked good varsity. Billy you may want to pull your elbows in more. Otherwise you look great. John, good pace, though you may want to lift your head up when you run. Daniel, you are much better than what you are showing. You have the ability to run in the front. Max, I know your natural pace is faster. You can run 60 seconds in your sleep."

"Why don't you shut up, Caleb!" The exclamation came from Reed, the leader of the varsity team. "You're not a member of this team! Go back up to the stands and watch how it's done!"

Caleb looked up with a smile and calmly replied, "You're right Reed. I'm not a member of this team. But, I have been sitting back and observing 'how it's done' in Reed's world. The only reason you are ahead of the pack is due to bullying. You're a good runner, but for some reason you are afraid of these new guys. You feel the only way you can beat them on the track is to beat them off the track. You're better than that."

Even though Caleb's pill of truth was coated with affirmation, Reed didn't take it very well. At first he glanced over at the coach for help, but the round little man simply stood quietly, interested to see what would transpire. Reed didn't know what to say, so Caleb helped him out. "I know I'm not on the team, but I'll challenge you to a race. If you win, you'll never see me again. If I win, you stop bullying."

Once again Reed looked over at his coach who was totally enthralled now and nodding. "What type race?"

Caleb looked at him with a wicked smile. "I know the 400 is your best race, so we will do it."

"Easy enough. Do you need a head start?"

Caleb laughed and then looked over to Daniel for a moment. "No need for that, but let's make it more interesting. Let's make it a two-man relay race. Daniel and I will take on you and Billy. He is the next fastest guy on the team. Daniel and Billy will take the first 400 and we will race the last 400."

"Reed looked back in relief and wonderment. "We will kill you."

"We'll see." Caleb walked over and pulled Daniel to the side. "I need you to run like I know you can. Billy is trained to run behind Reed. He's awkward when he's in the lead. Get a good start, cruise behind him until the 300 mark and then blow him away." With wide eyes his friend looked back and nodded.

Daniel and Billy took their batons and walked up to the starting line. The coach stepped up and yelled, "On your mark, get set, go!" Billy took off in the lead and Daniel tucked in behind him. Not accustomed to being in the lead and nervous with Daniel on his heels, Billy sped up even more on the backside. By the time he reached the 300 mark he was at full speed and unaware that Daniel had just kicked it in. As the two rounded the last curve and raced towards Reed and Caleb, Daniel pulled ahead. By the time he handed the baton to Caleb he was five meters ahead of Billy.

Everyone expected Caleb to explode off the line, but instead he merely took the baton and jogged ahead and stopped. He turned and looked back at Reed who grabbed the baton from Billy and raced past him. Caleb allowed him to get five strides ahead and then like a predator he pounced. The coach watched in amazement as Caleb caught up with Reed at the 200 mark, but instead of passing him he pulled up right next to him and began to talk. "You know Reed, you're a good runner, but you could be so much better if you would let the others challenge you." And then Caleb sprinted away as if Reed was standing still. By the time Reed crossed the line Caleb was buried under a mound of newbies celebrating his victory. After several pats on the back, Caleb emerged and walked over to Reed and offered his hand. "Good run." Reed remained quiet, but did shake his hand. Caleb accepted it and turned to see the coach staring him down with his crossed arms resting on his plump belly. "Son, you owe me for all these shenanigans. When I agreed to let you help me, this is not what I had in mind."

"Sorry for the disruption, Coach. How can I make it up to you?"

"You can leave...But tomorrow when you show up for practice be dressed and ready to run. Reed and Daniel need to be pushed. And Caleb, bring that attitude back. This team needs a captain who believes in them."

Chapter 7

ADMIRATION

Saturday – June 30, 1990
7:16 PM
Southern Fork Trail

WILL dug through his pack until he found his food bag. It had grown so skinny that it was now harder to find. Pulling it out, he quickly reached in and snagged the last two items – a fruit pastry and a pack of dried noodles. This was the first time on the trip that his food supply had dwindled down to such a pitiful degree. Fortunately, tomorrow he would hit a trail town and be able to re-supply. Until then, he had noodles for dinner and a pastry for breakfast.

As Will whipped out his stove and fuel, he looked over at Alex who was just now making it into camp. "You feel okay Alex?"

Alex looked up at him, but there seemed to be no one home. After a long pause he finally muttered, "I'm good."

Will noticed his friend's hand had a shake to it as he walked by. "You sure? You just look a little flustered. Did you get a sip of bad water?"

Alex suddenly turned and lashed out, "I said I'm good! Now leave me alone! You're not my mother!" Will quietly surrendered and watched Alex stumble to the far end of the clearing and drop his pack.

This outburst was just a cherry on an already odd last few days. Ever since his unusual talk with Alex, he had noticed him pulling away. Since then, conversation had become minimal. As a matter of fact all interaction had become strained.

Will replayed in his mind every encounter he had with Alex in the last few days trying to recall where he may have made him mad. Growing up, his grandmother had stressed to him Philippians 4:8 and how he should not only think of things that were admirable, true and pure, but his actions should also be admirable, true and pure. He could still hear his Mamaw say, "Behave in such a way so that your friends will like you for the right reasons and your enemies will hate you for the wrong ones."

After a quick dinner, Will saw no point in pushing for conversation around the fire. Alex had already retired to his tent, so Will hung his pack on a tree, leaned his staff up against it, and crawled into his hammock. He soon drifted off to sleep. He slept soundly as he always did on the trail after a long day's hike, but he had also developed a keen sense of alertness. Sometime in the early morning before the sun rose, he sensed movement just beyond his hammock. With his hand on his knife, he peered over to see Alex fully packed and ready to leave. Will remained silent as he watched Alex slowly sneak over to his own backpack and start rummaging through it. Within seconds he found Will's wallet. He flipped through it, counting the cash and the cards, and then simply stuck it in his pocket. Less than a minute later he was gone.

Monday – September 27. 2010
8:32 am
Sunrise Youth Development Center

Nothing fast ever happened at Sunrise Youth Development Center, especially anything that depended on paperwork that had to travel through the many layers of bureaucracy that clogged the government institution. That's why it was no surprise to Matthew when, after several weeks of being in a basic reading and math class, he was called out one Monday morning by the principal. "We just got your transcripts from your high school and it appears you are too smart for this class. Would you agree Mr. Harris?"

Matthew gave a slight shrug, "Not to sound rude, sir, but I didn't know you had smarter classes. I figured here Run Pug Run was at the upper echelon of academia."

"Upper echelon, aye? That does it. You're headed to Mr. Mullen's class."

Matthew was escorted down a hall he had never seen before and into a room with less than a dozen other students. As the principal spoke with the teacher, Matthew looked around the room and recognized but one face. "I see you're still stalking me," said Benjamin with a smirk.

"What is this class?"

"It's not a class, it's a torture chamber," stated Benjamin with little emotion other than the touch of disdain he was unable to hold back. Matthew looked at Benjamin and then to Mr. Mullen who was now walking over.

"Benjamin is correct," smiled Mr. Mullen. "Everyday you come in I will be prying your heads open and scraping every bit of brain cells I can find to mold into something useful. The highest expectations we have for most residents here at the Center is a GED, but my students will be prepared for high school graduation and college."

"Which is totally useless considering no one here can afford college," interrupted Benjamin. "We would be better off settling for a GED."

Mr. Mullen looked at him and shook his head. "Benjamin is convinced he can never rise to become more than what he is right now."

"That's right. I'm going to be a thug all my life," exclaimed Benjamin with as much resolve as he could muster.

Matthew looked at him and then burst out laughing. "I just realized I like you. You're the most hilarious thug I've ever met. Can you look at me real seriously and say, 'I'm thugilicious'?"

Benjamin's smirk curled into a grin. "Have they upped your meds? If not, they need to."

"Oh Ben, your bubbly spirit is intoxicating enough."

At this point Mr. Mullen interrupted, "Here's what

I'm thinking. If you score higher than anyone else during the next six weeks, I'll let you settle for a GED. As a matter of fact, I'll administer it and when you pass, you can move out of my class and into Mr. Bohn's shovel crew."

Benjamin thought about it for a second, "I would rather be raking leaves outside than sitting in this classroom. You've got a deal." The student and teacher shook on it, and then Benjamin sat back in his desk happy with himself. It would have been the happiest moment since arriving at the pen had it not been for Matthew's continuous laughter. Benjamin tried to ignore it, but then he couldn't take it anymore. "What is so freakin funny?"

"He tricked you!" laughed Matthew. "It's fixed and you fell for it."

Benjamin rethought it for a second. "How is it fixed? I've been the top student since I arrived here amongst these brainless twits."

Matthew looked at him and smiled, "But not since I arrived and I'm so much smarter than you!"

Benjamin smiled, "Is that right?"

"Unequivocally."

"We will see, my friend."

Friday – October 15, 2010
2:37 PM
A few blocks from Big State University

"Mrs. Evans!"

"Yes dear?"

"When are the cookies going to be ready?"

"I'm getting them out of the oven right now." Mrs. Evans homemade cookies had become a tradition at the children's home dating back 35 years ago when she first started working there. She had long since retired and now only volunteered on Fridays or Saturdays or Sundays, or whenever her sore back told her she could do so. Snatching up rug rats and bending over and giving too many hugs had taken its toll on her body. She knew her doctor would tell her to stay home and rest, but then she would miss out on cool autumn days like today that flooded her mind with precious memories and in turn lightened her heart and strengthened her spirit.

No sooner had she pulled the cookies out of the oven and set them on the counter to cool than a little hand reached up out of nowhere and attempted to grab one. "Owww! It hurts! Why did you make them so hot!"

"They're hot because I haven't sprinkled them with magic and said the magic word. You know that is how it works, Samuel."

"I forgot. What is the magic word?"

"I don't know if your magic skills are quite ready...." Just then Mrs. Evans heard what sounded like screaming in the front yard followed by a car door slamming. By the time she made it to the window, all she saw was a car driving off and a familiar face making her way inside. She continued to listen as the sound of kids greeting their visitor echoed through the old house louder and louder until the crowd of munchkins emerged through the doorway with an unscarfed Rose leading the way. "Just in time for cookies."

"But they're not ready!" exclaimed Samuel with

so much passion you would have thought they were poisonous. Rose ignored him and walked directly to the pantry and pulled out the sugar bowl. With a quick scoop she sprinkled the cookies and yelled, "Allakazam Boppity Boop!"

Samuel looked at the cookies and then over to Mrs. Evans. "Are they ready?"

"Yes, Samuel. But remember to share, because if you eat too many…"

"My head will pop off like a balloon and float out the window," finished Samuel.

While all the kids surrounded the cookies, Mrs. Evans called Rose over. "What was all that ruckus about in the front yard?"

"I'm being stalked by a crazy girl," shared Rose.

"Well don't stop there. Who is she and why is she stalking you?"

"I don't know. I mean…well, her name is Andrea…I think. And I don't know why she suddenly took an interest in me. A few weeks ago she was making fun of me and now she wants to be my friend."

"So what was going on in the front yard just now?" asked Mrs. Evans.

"She wanted to give me a ride from school and when I refused, she followed me here. She was also saying she wanted me to join her at a retreat or something. I think she's part of a cult."

"What do your other friends think about her?" The question seemed to hit Rose unexpectedly as she paused and glanced away. The reaction didn't hinder Mrs. Evans one iota. "You have talked about this to them…your friends?"

Rose now stared sharply at Mrs. Evans, "My friends don't care about such things."

This wasn't Mrs. Evans first staring contest, so she looked back very softly, but steadily. "Really Rose? I can't imagine true friends not being concerned about such things."

"Well, my friends have more important things to be worried about."

"I see," continued the old woman. "Like hot cookies and who will tuck them in at night?"

"These kids understand me!"

Mrs. Evans reached out and took Rose by the hand. "These kids understand tragedy and loss and living with a disability. But, Rose, you are more than that scar on your face. You were someone special before the car accident and the loss of your parents, and you are still someone special. That person needs friends too. Friends who understand college life, and boyfriends, and all the other fascinating and frustrating things that happen at your age."

Rose fought it for a brief moment, but then started to lightly cry. "I don't have friends like that. I can't have friends like that."

"The only thing preventing such friendship to blossom is you. Like it or not, you have to be friendly to get friends. That means you will need to open up to people and possibly become vulnerable."

"I'm afraid people won't like me," sobbed Rose.

"Sadly, you will meet some people who don't

appreciate you and visa versa. There are some people who will annoy and aggravate you. That's chemistry, but that's also why there are millions of people in the world. You are a terrific young lady with a wonderful heart. You will draw those same type people towards you."

"I don't know," sighed Rose.

"Really Rose? You just had a lady who wants to be your friend so bad that she is stalking you and wanting you to become a member of her cult. Trust me. Cult friends are loyal and don't care about scars."

Rose started giggling, "I guess you're right."

"You know I'm right," laughed Mrs. Evans. "Just don't drink the kool-aid. They're not going to be your friend after the kool-aid drinking anyway."

Friday – October 26, 2010
4:45 PM
Camp Nick-a-Lou

Camp Nick-a-Lou had been the fall retreat location for the Christian Student Center for as long as Jess could remember. Her older brother had attended here several years earlier and often spoke about how fun the retreats were and how spiritually uplifting it was to see hundreds of people attend. Jess didn't personally know anything about that. Ever since she arrived at the CSC, the core group had been small and the fall retreat was simply a small gathering where people came to talk about others.

This year was already turning out to be different. A number of the students had arrived a couple days earlier with Mr. George to attend a Challenge Point teambuilding workshop. Now most had returned to campus to help pick up others. Jess had caught an early ride with Lance and now they sat on the deck watching others arrive.

"So who all came to the Challenge Point thingy?" asked Lance as he kicked his feet up on the railing.

"I don't know," replied Jess. "I'm sure Lisa was there ruling over everything."

"That's why I didn't want anything to do with it. I just don't like her, and those two new dweebs she's always with Donny and Casey."

"It's Daniel and Caleb, and they're not dweebs. They're too handsome to be dweebs."

Lance looked at her and began gagging. "They're not that good looking. Let's switch subjects so that I don't vomit my lunch. Where is Andrea?"

"I haven't spoken with her in a while."

"Aren't you two roommates?"

"No, she moved out. After her family scandal, she couldn't afford our place anymore. I don't know where she is now."

"Good riddance," sneered Lance. "I was tired of her constant whining anyway. Hey, it looks like someone is finally arriving."

As Mr. George drove the bus up and parked, he was physically tired and yet mentally so excited he doubted he would be able to sleep tonight. The last two days had gone far better than he had ever dreamed. In his mind his prayers had been answered when Lisa, Caleb, Daniel, Andrea and several others showed up for the two-day leadership workshop and had passionately taken ownership of the ministry. He felt even more blessed when he returned to the Center and discovered a crowd of students ready to come to the retreat. All of his prayers were being answered. "Do you need help unpacking, Mr. George?"

"That would be great, Caleb."

"Did you hear that guys? Let's get to work." While the other students filed off the bus and went to explore the grounds, Caleb, Daniel and all the track team members they had invited went to work unloading food, luggage, and everything else.

"You invited us on this trip and now you're making us work?" asked Max with a smile.

"Work? You think this is work? Wait until you hit the kitchen," said Caleb.

"What do you mean?" asked Billy.

"Daniel, how many people are going to be here?" asked Caleb.

"Oh, at least a hundred, maybe two."

"Wow!" exclaimed Caleb. "That's a lot of meals you're going to be cooking."

Lance and Jess watched from a distance as car after car began arriving and waves of people began pouring into the lodge. "Good grief! I've never seen half these people," groaned Lance. "Is that Andrea?"

Jess sat up and looked closer, "It is. I can't believe she showed up."

"Who is she with? I've never seen her before."

"I don't know, but she has a terrible scar on her face. That just shows you how far down the social ladder Andrea has fallen."

"And who are those goofy guys?" whined Lance. "Who are they laughing at?"

"That's your university's track team and they are laughing at themselves," said Mr. George as he suddenly walked up from behind. "That's what friends often do when they enjoy one another's company."

That evening, after everyone had settled in and played Monarch and Asteroids and Parachute Sharks, they shared a meal together and then gathered in the main lodge to sing and pray. It had been years since Rose had been to church. She had lost faith after the loss of her parents and later the incarceration of her brother. And while she still wasn't quite ready to pray to God, she did enjoy the singing and the company of Andrea and her newest acquaintance, Lisa. They sang for almost an hour before Mr. George got up in front of the group. "If you've not heard me say it three times already, welcome to our fall retreat. If this is your first time here, you are in good company. It's mine too. I moved here six months ago to take on this position as campus minister. To be honest, the first few months here I was not too thrilled about what I had gotten myself into. But, in the last few weeks I've seen some remarkable works of the Spirit and I know God placing me here is a true blessing. Much of that remarkable change occurred after my old friend, Mr. Barrow spoke about relationships. That night he spoke about the first six As – Acknowledgement, Alcatraz, Abhorrence, Apathy, Acceptance, and Affirmation. This weekend he is here to speak with us about the final three As – Admiration, Action, and Accountability.

Chapter 8

THE FINAL THREE

Admiration - *"I actually like you. There are characteristics about you that I admire."*

OCCASIONALLY you will meet someone you actually like. This means you enjoy their company. You find them funny, intelligent, or possibly charming. There is some quality about this person that you appreciate.

As I've stated before, liking or disliking someone is a feeling. It is based off of personal chemistry. Unlike the previous steps, where you intentionally accept a person no matter what, and you do your best to build them up even if they have few qualities you appreciate, you cannot make yourself like someone. If your personalities clash or there is nothing likable about the other person, there is not much you can do about it. The good news is as long as your standards are not ridiculously high to the point that the human race disgusts you, throughout your life there should be lots of people you enjoy being around.

The realm of Admiration is much like a swimming pool. There is a shallow end and a deep end. In the shallow end you will find people whom you find pleasant to be around. You enjoy their personality and are not repulsed to be in their presence.

In the deeper end of Admiration are people who you truly admire. There are qualities about their character that you find admirable, and you spend time with them in an effort to make those qualities your own. You allow these people to have an influence over you. They may be family members, peers or mentors.

From Acknowledgement to Admiration

It is possible to meet someone and experience 'like' at first sight. From the moment you meet, a spark is there and chemistry is great. You quickly play off of each other like you have known each other all your life. Then again, some relationships must spend quite a bit of time in Acceptance and Affirmation before you move into Admiration. Every relationship is different.

You may know of people who, when they first met, didn't like each other at all. They were one step away from Abhorrence, or knee deep in it, when through a shared experience, jubilant or tragic, they discovered that they do like each other. This often happens with people who are too much alike. These people often share the same negative qualities in their personalities and it's not until they are able to mutually understand that fact that they learn to appreciate the other.

Whether Admiration is instant or not, the rules of Acceptance and Affirmation are still necessary for that relationship to continue to grow. Acceptance and encouragement comes more easily if you actually appreciate that person.

Influence

Compared to previous steps, influence becomes a true factor when a relationship reaches Admiration. During Acceptance and Affirmation, influence is often an offensive game. You are doing your best to influence them positively. Concerning Admiration, it is possible that you will be influenced as much as, or more than you influence.

Of course, the amount of influence is dependent on how deep into Admiration the relationship exists. If this is someone whom you are consciously altering your own behavior to mimic theirs, then their influence is certainly strong over you. It is not a bad thing (depending on the behavior). It is how we grow and develop into the people we ultimately desire to be. Whether consciously or unconsciously, our own aspirations draw us towards individuals with the characteristics needed to reach our goals. Along the way, we pick up behaviors and skills needed to accomplish those goals.

Sounds easy, but unfortunately people also have a weaker or darker side to their character and are often drawn towards those people who feed that side as well. As a general rule, just as lowering the bar is easier than raising the bar, darker traits are easier to pick up and to ingrain into our character. And thus we have the internal battle between good and evil. Do I crawl or do I fly?

The Christian Perspective

If you ask most Christians what is the most basic concept of friendship they will likely quote the first part of the King James Version of Proverbs 18:24 – "A man who has friends must show himself to be friendly." I doubt anyone can argue that. Scripture both encourages forming friendships, and it also warns us about developing poor friendships. Proverbs 12:26 – "A righteous man is cautious in friendship, but the way of the wicked leads them astray."

Scripture recognizes that relationships in the Admiration realm are influential in shaping who we are and what path we will choose. Friends influence our behavior and our decisions. This always reminds me of Philippians 4:8 – "Finally brothers, whatever is true, whatever is noble, whatever is right, whatever is pure, whatever is lovely, whatever is admirable – if anything is excellent or praiseworthy – think about such things." I like to translate that into, "Finally when seeking out friends, search out those who are true, and noble, right and pure; seek those who search for excellence and that which is praiseworthy – seek fellowship with such individuals."

I realize 'like' is a feeling and not always under your control however, I do believe that your character is magnetic and attracts similar character. It is also completely in your power whom you decide to emulate.

It is your decision how deep a person goes in the pool of Admiration.

By the way, if you are young and have no Christian mentors, you need them. If you are older and have no protégés, then you need to fulfill your role as a mentor. To the young, I suggest seeking out those older individuals who possess qualities you admire and spend time with them. Ask them questions and treasure their answers. Their wisdom can save you several hardships. Older people, make yourself available and don't be afraid to share your story. You are wiser than you believe.

The Leadership Perspective

Everyone needs friends, especially those in leadership. If you are a charismatic leader you will attract people to you. Most will come to you for the right reason; some for their own selfish reasons. As a leader you need to be proactive in deciding who stays at the Affirmation level compared to those you allow in the deep end of the Admiration pool.

The key is to make sure relationships at the Admiration level are true friendships. The first step in this process is to make sure you know who you are and what you stand for. Don't waiver. Good friendships will support you and make you better. The poisonous ones will try to tear that foundation down and warp your sense of who you are. Always be aware of a friend's impact on you. Ask yourself, why you see them as your friend. What is it that you like about them and what is it that they like about you? Are they making you a better person? Don't be surprised if people are using you for your influential power. Remember, while you may be blessed with several friends, too many can lead to your downfall. In life, you can't make everyone happy.

One final reason to be proactive about who is at this level, is you need to surround yourself with people who will challenge you and inspire you. We will talk about this more in the next levels, but take note that you are not a finished product. You need mentors to train you, dreamers to inspire you and true friends with tough skin to keep you in line. You can't buy them at Wal-Mart. They have to be filtered in through the pool of Admiration.

The Two-Way Road

As I said from the beginning, relationships require two people and can be seen from two different viewpoints. While one person may be apathetic towards a relationship, the other may be making the effort to be affirming at every encounter. While one person is accepting the other may be struck with admiration. Relationships up to this point can have any number of combinations. From this point onward though, for a relationship to grow beyond Admiration, both individuals must be in agreement. If you both don't like each other and appreciate each others qualities, there is no moving on to the Action level.

Action - "I am always here for you. I have your back."

True friendships are the greatest gifts on this earth. Every great story is packed with them. Han Solo and Chewbacca, Frodo and Sam, Huckleberry Finn and Tom

Sawyer, Xena and Gabrielle, Woody and Buzz Lightyear, Laverne and Shirley, Harry Potter and Ron Weasley, Lucy and Ethel, Kirk and Spock, Thelma and Louise, Sherlock Holmes and Dr. Watson, Oprah and Gayle, Robin Hood and Little John, and don't forget Phineas and Ferb with their 104 days of summer. No one questions whether these people are friends. It's been proven over and over. They are all Action level friends.

Friendships at this depth go beyond words. No longer do you have to tell him that you love him. It is shown on a continual basis through action. These are the friends who are always there for you. If you are broken down on the side of the road, they are who you call on. If you got in a fight, they have your back. If you pooped your pants in school, they give you their underwear, no questions asked.

Action level relationships are not fragile. You can fuss, fight and argue with them and afterwards the relationship is as strong as ever. If you make a horrible mistake and destroy your reputation, Action level friends will be there by your side to pick you up. These friendships have been tempered through fire and covered in forgiveness.

Action level friends are also usually brought together by a third force. Sometimes it is a shared experience or tragedy that draws them together. It can be a shared purpose or mission bigger than the both of them. It can be a spiritual bond, a sports achievement, a career connection, or simply the need to save the earth. Such a bond holds these friends together when their personalities push them apart. It forces them to meld together and change that which would create a chasm in their relationship.

For most of us, life has many chapters that take place in different locations. There may be people whom you were extremely close to in high school, college, or in the military and due to having to move, you rarely ever see each other any more. Action level friends are those that time has no effect on. After years of being away, the moment you meet you simply pick up where you left off.

From Acknowledgement to Action

Action level friendships are built on trust and loyalty that has been paved through a history of time and energy spent together. You don't go immediately from Acknowledgement to Action level. There is a long honeymoon period where you get to know each other and test one another and see what the other is truly made of. Good times and bad times, fun times and boring times are spent together. Due to the time and energy required to forge a relationship like this, not every friendship makes it this far. It requires a special chemistry and a special commitment.

Influence

Friendships at this depth carry with them a great amount of influence. These people are your inner circle and often you will be making the same decisions just so you can go down the same road together. There is no denying that due to the time and energy you sacrifice for each other, you play a part in shaping one another.

The Christian Perspective

Deep friendship or brotherhood is certainly something encouraged within scripture. Ecclesiastes 4:9-12 – "Two are better than one, because they have a good return for their work: If one falls down, his friend can help him up. But pity the fool who falls and has no one to help him up! Also, if two lie together, they will keep warm, but how can one keep warm alone? Though one may be overpowered, two can defend themselves. A cord of three strands is not quickly broken."

Life is filled with good times and bad times. If given the choice, most would always choose the happy moments, but the tough times have their benefits. Proverbs 17:17 – "A friend loves at all times and a brother is born for adversity." Proverbs 18:24 – "A man of many companions may come to ruin, but there is a friend who sticks closer than a brother."

In the same way iron is forged in extreme heat to burn away the impurities, when bad times roll in you are given an opportunity to see who really is willing to stand by your side and support you. Just like with Jonathan and David, Action level friends are there to help you even after all other friends and family have left you.

As a Christian, be aware that these individuals you allow in your inner circle will have a great influence on your character and ultimately on your life. I would encourage that you serve the same Lord and are traveling down the same spiritual path. You don't want there to be a day when you have to choose between your closest friend or your God. On the other hand, you do not want to go through life without a handful of Action level friends. They are a true gift from God and for you to become what God wants, you will need them.

The Leadership Perspective

If you think of everyone who calls you friend and you are not able to know unquestionably those who are Action level friends, then you are in trouble. You need these people in your life. At some point, you will falter and you will need these people to help you. Spend the time and energy needed to develop these closer bonds. It will require a sacrifice of your schedule and you will need to become more vulnerable with them than you are with your regular acquaintances, but you need them for your inner circle. When people criticize you and try to tear you down, your inner circle will be there to encourage you. And, when you've gotten too much praise and your head is beginning to swell, these true friends are there to clear the hot air and put your feet back on the ground.

Accountability - "We have a transparent relationship. I know your strengths and weaknesses."

One would think that Action would be the deepest level, but I would argue that Accountability is even deeper. To trust someone unquestionably with the workings of your life is tough, but to trust someone with the inner workings of your soul is even tougher. Accountability relationships are the inner circle of the inner circle.

With these elite individuals you share a transparent relationship, meaning there are no secrets or rooms of the soul that they cannot look into and clean out if need be. Accountability level friends know your strengths and weaknesses. They know your dreams and ultimate fears. They know the true you.

These friends not only understand you, but they serve the purpose of helping to guide you. If you are about to head down a path that leads to your destruction, they step in and stop you. They serve as a listening ear, a comforting shoulder, wise counsel, and when need be, a stiff boot to kick you back into reality.

From Acknowledgement to Accountability

In the same way Action friends don't just happen, Accountability relationships take time to develop. Trust is built over a long period of time and even after someone reaches the Action level, creating transparency takes even more time. Just because a friend is helpful doesn't mean you are ready to reveal your deepest, darkest secrets. It takes more time. Often people will share a small secret and see how their friends deal with it. If confidence is kept and the friendship is unaffected by the knowledge, more secrets are revealed. Once again, this is a two-way street and reaching the point where you know everything about each other takes time. When you are twelve, one pillow party may do the job, but as you grow older you and your life grow more complex.

Influence

Accountability friends have the strongest amount of influence. Their authority comes from that which they have earned and you have granted them. They are there in that position because you elected them to be and not for any other reason.

The counsel of these friends is deeply important. For instance, if I was doing something unquestionably wrong that I strongly desired to do anyway and someone whom I just met pointed it out to me, I would likely not listen to him. As a matter of fact, I would chew him up and spit him out. I would likely not listen to anyone from the Acceptance or Affirmation stages. From my viewpoint those people don't know me and understand my position. I may give a slight pause if they are at the Admiration level, but it would actually take an Accountability level relationship to stop me in my tracks and change my direction. They've been tested. They know me and love me. I know they have my best interest at heart. I respect them and I trust their counsel.

The Christian Perspective

Christianity is not a solo journey. It is a life trek that can only be done with the fellowship of those heading to the same destination. Along the way you need guidance, inspiration, comfort, training, protection, and love. You need the person who can stand shoulder to shoulder with you, and if need be, go toe to toe with you. Accountability friends protect you from the world and from yourself.

Just as life changes with the seasons, as Christians, if we are growing to become more Christ-like, then we are also changing. Growth is a social event. We need brothers and sisters who are there growing alongside of us and providing comfort, counsel, and challenge along the way. Proverbs 27:17 – "As iron sharpens iron, so one man sharpens another".

In high school and college I ran track. In high school I was the fastest around and never thought I would break my personal record. When I reached college and had fellow runners even faster than I was, I got faster. I needed them to challenge me to make me better.

Developing Accountability friendships is not easy. Beyond the time and effort required, it takes courage to open one's self up and to become vulnerable to another. Counsel from true friends, though covered in love, can still be hard to hear. It can also be difficult to give. Rebuking a loved one is not easy, but it is necessary when that person is doing something self-destructive. Proverbs 27:6 – "Faithful are the wounds of a friend, but the kisses of an enemy are deceitful".

My grandfather always said if you find five friends in your life who are true, and love you enough to tell you the truth, then you have lived a rich life. Accountability friends are the truest of friends and are the richest blessings in life.

The Leadership Perspective

History is littered with the stories of leaders who grew so powerful that they lost reality and believed themselves to be invulnerable. No one was there to tell them the difference, and ultimately, they destroyed themselves. Hollywood has such a wealth of train wreck tales about stars who drowned in their own fame, that there is an entire genre of shows dedicated to telling about their downfalls. Fame, power and wealth are not easily tamed and can destroy a person in a heartbeat.

While a leader needs to be a dreamer with aspirations, one must also have his feet rooted deeply to the ground. It's not a one-man job. It requires some special friends; people who know and love you - the person, and not you - the legend. Ones who are not hired or in any other way influenced to tell you what you want to hear. Friends who will stare you straight in the face and give you the truth, no matter how it makes you feel.

Money and power can give you as many cheerleaders as you can ever imagine, but only friendships created through time, energy, and personal sacrifice can produce counsel more precious than gold. In the same way you build your vision and your followers, take time to build those golden relationships that will ground you and bless you far more than anything else on this earth.

Full Circle

In a perfect world, every relationship you developed would always maintain its deepest roots and greatest heights. Admiration level friends would always be Admiration level and Action level friends would always be Action level. Unfortunately, relationships are created from people and just as they can grow and blossom, they can diminish and sour.

That is the fluid nature of relationships. People change, and sometimes change has a negative effect on a relationship. People who were once very close may change the direction of their lives and, therefore, grow apart. People whom we once knew so well can change their character and personality to the point we no longer recognize them. Life experiences, environments, and the influence of other relationships can change people and affect the relationship we have with them.

Should you pursue relationships if they are possibly going to fall apart? Are you just setting yourself up to get hurt? Is it worth it? The answer is yes, yes, and yes. I hope you pursue a life that is rich in relationships. I hope those relationships bring you every emotion that God has blessed us with – the good and the bad. Joy is great, but joy after sorrow is even richer. Through sorrow and suffering you grow and become stronger and wiser. You learn to appreciate the good things in life that you may have otherwise overlooked and in the big picture, those matured perspectives makes the hard lessons worth it. The bottom line is don't let the fear of rejection and sorrow prevent you from experiencing the joys of relationships. Unlike superficial friendships that are sugar coated, but fragile, true friendships have weathered through a wide spectrum of emotions and have strong roots anchored deep within a myriad of good and bad experiences.

The key to maintaining relationships is to never let it be consumed with hate or apathy to the point that it is not valuable. You and your closest friend may have a falling out to the point that not only are you no longer there for each other, but you don't even like each other. The pain may be so bad that you cannot think of one good thing to say about her and if you let your wounded heart come to full rage, the relationship would go straight into Abhorrence.

This is where once again you have to make a decision and set forth a conscious mindset. Is this person of such pitiful disregard that I can say they are of no value whatsoever? From the Christian perspective can you say this person is unworthy of love? Keep in mind that while we were yet sinners, God sent His most valuable Son to die so that He may have a relationship with us. Is this person, compared to you, any less worthy than you are to God?

It is my hope you will never allow a relationship to drop below Acceptance. It is the rich neutral ground of basic value. And chances are, given time and healing, that same relationship may grow once again. People change, and so do we. Where once we were fragile and easily upset by the least imperfections of our friends, we grow more loving and tolerant, and value greater those treasures that we once were so quick to throw away. Given a second, or third time to re-grow, that relationship comes back even more mature than before. That is the beauty of relationships.

Chapter 9

ACTION

Sunday – July 1, 1990
1:12 PM
Trail Town on Southern Fork Trail

THIS day had all the potential to be the worst in Alex's life. He felt terrible in every way imaginable. His head thumped with pain as the withdrawals grew in severity. His heart ached with a guilt he had never felt. He still couldn't believe he robbed the one person who wanted to be his friend. His body hurt all over, partly from the lack of drugs, but mostly from the ten mile hike he had just sprinted to reach this town and more specifically, this insidious alley.

There were several bars along this disreputable route with just as many shadowy individuals to haunt them. Alex knew his only hope in quenching his demon was within the grasp of such unsavory hooligans. How to go about shopping for what he needed was another matter.

At first he walked around simply watching, but it wasn't long before he felt eyes upon him.

"I got something for that shake," shared a seedy man who slithered out of nowhere.

Alex looked him in his beady eyes and then down at his own trembling hand. "W- w-what's it worth to you?"

"Depends on what you got and how much you need."

"How much will this buy?" foolishly asked Alex as he revealed his stash of cash.

"Oh," grinned the dirty fox. "That will buy a lot. More than I have right now. Tell you what; I'll meet you at the River Weasel Pub in an hour."

Just as he was instructed, an hour later Alex sat in a back corner booth at the grimy pub and awaited his delivery. Right on time his supplier showed up with two other guys at his side. "I got what you need," he grinned as he slipped from his sleeve a plastic pill bottle. "Do you have what I need?"

Alex reached in his pocket and pulled out the wad of cash and placed it on the table. Within seconds the man slapped it up and tossed Alex the bottle. "It was good doing business with you."

As the three scoundrels began to walk away, Alex opened the bottle only to see it filled with pebbles. The reality of his situation struck him and rage poured forth like madness. Without a second thought he lunged towards the thieves, only to be punched square in the face before he realized what hit him. The next few seconds went by slowly. Two men held him down and wailed on his face while the third kicked him in his abdomen. He counted three kicks when suddenly he heard the man scream. He opened his blackened eyes just in time to see a wooden staff come out of nowhere and crack the heads of both his assailants. "Come on Alex! Let's get out of here!" He looked up to see Will as he was jerked to his feet. The next thing he knew the two were in a mad rush that didn't stop until they were back in the woods along the trail.

Out of breath and bleeding, Alex collapsed against a tree. With his eyes closed, he secretly hoped Will would take a final few punches at him and leave. He deserved that and more. Instead, Will walked over with a wet bandana and began cleaning his open wounds. Alex struggled to know what to say. Thank you and I'm sorry both seemed inadequate at the moment. In the end it was Will who spoke. "Why didn't you tell me you had an addiction? I can help."

The struggle in Alex's shattered heart finally burst in a flood of tears, "I'm sorry!" he wailed. "I robbed you! I'm so sorry!"

"No harm done," comforted Will as he pulled from his pocket the wad of cash. "Sometimes friends need a little maintenance to get them back in sync."

Tuesday – October 26, 2010
7:00 PM
Sunrise Youth Development Center

The last few weeks had brought about lots of change for Ben. After Matthew had joined his class, the next day Ben had been in an altercation and was moved to the same living unit as Matthew. While Ben had made no friends with his old unit, moving to the new unit had not been the most wonderful of experiences. It came with a new schedule, new staff and a new counselor.

Ben had never been one to appreciate change. From past experiences, he connected change with things getting worse. His parents had died – that was a change. His time spent in foster care – that was a change. His little crime spree and time in lock-up – that was definitely a change.

"Benjamin!" called the guard. "It's your turn to do laundry!" Ben hopped up off his bed, grabbed his cloth sac that held all his dirty clothes, and stepped out into the hall where the guard pointed to the far end of the living unit and then walked back into his office. Ben took a deep breath, then began a most uncomfortable walk.

Changing units had not changed the fact that he was still a walking target. Every room he passed there was a thug staring back at him. Ben tried not to stare back and yet he also wanted to get a jump on the first one who sprang on him. Door after door he made his way, until finally he reached the end of the hall where the tiny laundry room awaited him. *This might be a bearable day after all.*

As the thought crossed his mind he heard a loud noise from the other end. He stuck his head out of the laundry room just in time to see four gang members bust into a big brawl. It puzzled him at first, but then it all became clear as three others started walking briskly towards him. The guards were so busy with the other four that they didn't see what was about to go down in the laundry room. Ben balled up his fist and braced for the impact. He watched as all three thugs stepped into the room with looks of hatred on their face. Ben was about to close his eyes and pray for survival when he saw Matthew flying into the room over them all. He landed right in the middle of the three hooligans with fists a flying. Ben couldn't believe it. He looked into the mound of flailing bodies and caught a glimpse of Matthew smiling back at him. *He's absolutely crazy!* Before he could even finish the thought he too jumped into the mash and swung away.

Half an hour later Ben and Matthew sat together in the infirmary. Both were bruised and bloodied. Only Matthew had a cut on his arm that would require stitches. Fortunately it missed anything vital. The nurse looked both of them over and then walked away to gather his supplies. For the first time the two were alone and staring at each other. "Why did you do that?" asked Ben. "Why did you throw yourself into that bunch?"

For once, Matthew looked at him very seriously. "They were going to hurt my friend and I couldn't allow that."

"Yes, but they could have easily killed you. One of the guys had a shank for crying out loud! He cut you!"

Matthew never changed the look on his face, but his stare became stronger and more penetrating. "They were going to hurt my friend and I couldn't allow that."

"But," struggled Ben as he tried to wrap his mind around Matthew's sacrifice.

"But nothing," replied Matthew as his seriousness melted into a warm grin. "They were going to hurt my friend and I couldn't allow that."

Saturday – December 4, 2010
1:20 PM
A few blocks from Big State University

Rose stood in the drug store on the candy aisle trying to decide between a giant bag of peppermint or butter scotch. *I have not seen the kids in over a week and I'm afraid they won't forgive me! Oh how I wish I could afford chocolate!* Rose finally grabbed the bag of peppermint on the idea that Christmas was rapidly approaching and this was the closest they would come to candy canes this year.

As she bought the candy and left the store she continued to fret. *I hate this season! It's bad enough they don't get much throughout the year, but now they have to go through a holiday of false hope where they see others getting things they can only dream of. And here I am, one of their favorites, and I've basically abandoned them! I had to take Mrs. Evans advice and build a social life. Now I feel terrible!*

Rose scurried down the same old roads she always took, but this time as she approached the children's home she noticed cars lining the street. *That's strange. What could be going on in this neighborhood?* When she reached the home she was even more surprised. Up on the roof and in the trees she saw guys hanging Christmas lights. *What are they doing?* At first she tried to get their attention, but they were busy and only one guy acknowledged her presence with a quick, "Merry Christmas!"

Hoping to get answers, Rose rushed on inside. Opening the door she expected to be greeted by the kids, but to her astonishment they were not there. Instead there were college students decorating the old home from room to room. She walked around in silent amazement until she came to the main room where a pine tree touched the 10 foot ceiling. In the midst of decorating it stood Andrea and Lisa. Rose remained frozen and silent until finally Andrea noticed her. "Oh great! You made it!"

"What is going on?" asked Rose.

Andrea looked around at all the decorations, "Well, it's not Halloween..."

"I get the Christmas theme, but why?"

"It's Christmas?"

Rose looked more frustrated than ever. "I get it, but why are you here?"

Lisa stepped in. "Rose, we know you care deeply for these kids, and therefore we care greatly for them. Andrea shared with us about the home and we thought we would come out and help."

Rose was on the verge of tears of appreciation, but still she could not cover her worry for the kids. "This is all nice, but in the end I'm afraid it will cause more harm than good. You're giving them false hope. They are going to believe Santa will now bring them gifts and that's never going to happen."

Andrea ran her hands through her hair and was about to speak when she suddenly grabbed Rose and pulled her down the hall and into a smaller den. There sat all the kids huddled around the feet of Santa Claus and a couple of his elves. One by one the elves picked them up and sat them on Santa's lap. "We're not a one-time visitor," smiled Andrea. "We're making a list and checking it twice. They will all get Christmas gifts this year."

"How can you afford that?" questioned Rose.

"Lisa and I are not the only ones who believe in what you are doing here. There are hundreds of us."

Overwhelmed with emotion, Rose burst into tears as she gave Andrea a big hug. "How can I make this up to you?"

"Honey, it's not about owing anyone anything. You are my closest friend, and this is just the way things roll."

Rose looked at her and smiled, "I understand."

Andrea then glanced over at the strapping college guy dressed as Santa, "One thing you could do though is help me find the mistletoe."

Friday – December 17, 2010
7:25 PM
Big State University

Caleb sat quietly in his room. He had spent the better part of the day packing up to go home for Christmas break. The entire dorm which was usually alive and bustling with activity was now eerily silent. Most everyone had left the day before. Caleb though, was stretching his departure date as far as he could.

Sitting on his bed, he reached into his nightstand drawer and pulled out a picture of his mother. When he first arrived it was displayed squarely on his desk, but in time he had grown unable to look at it. For a time he had been able to lock it away and pretend the pain no longer existed. That time had run out and now he was on a collision with all those wounds of the heart.

Just over six months ago his mother had been shot

and killed while on her way back from the grocery store. She had made the trip to get food for Caleb's high school graduation party. It was a trip that he should have been on as well, had it not been for his scuffle with Max. Wrestling with guilt and every other dark emotion springing from the depth of his battered conscience, Caleb almost didn't hear his phone as it began to ring and violently vibrate. "Hello."

"Hey, it's Daniel. Please tell me you haven't left campus yet."

"You're in luck. I'm the last one here. What's wrong?"

"I was on my way to visit my grandmother for Christmas when my car broke down. Could you come pick me up?"

"I'm insulted that you felt you had to ask. Where are you?"

Daniel gave him directions and soon Caleb was driving through the snow on the way to pick up his friend. Secretly he hoped this would lead to a complete white out where he had to spend the holiday with Daniel and his family instead of returning to his own home. At Thanksgiving, Caleb and Daniel had both opted out of going home and instead spent it with the other students at the Christian Student Center who were too far away from home to make the trip. During all that time together, neither had shared much about their family life, and as far as Caleb was concerned, that's what made the relationship work.

Fifteen miles outside of the city limits, Caleb spotted Daniel's car on the side of the road and pulled over next to it. Daniel immediately ran over and jumped in. "Hey buddy," said Caleb while Daniel flipped the heat on high blast. "Thanks for coming," replied Daniel as he struggled to get warm. "Once again, I'm insulted that you thought I wouldn't drive the length of the state to come help you. Is there anything we can do to fix the car?"

"It's dead, and beyond my knowledge," replied Daniel. "I'll deal with it later. Do you mind driving me to my grandmother's place? I'm late."

"I will if you promise to stop with the insults."

"Okay. Did I mention it's another 20 miles?"

The two drove through the snowy night, neither speaking of the challenges that awaited them. Instead they reflected back on all the experiences they had shared in the last few months and how it had drawn them closer. They contemplated and often laughed about the possibilities that lay ahead in the near future in regards to the track team and the Christian Student Center. Still, it seemed for both that they were dancing around a large elephant strapped with dynamite. Each had something to share and neither had the guts to do so.

"Is this it?" asked Caleb as they pulled into the parking lot of an assisted living residence. "We are here," replied Daniel somewhat hesitantly.

"Do you need me to come in?" asked Caleb. "I don't mind."

"Thanks, but you've been enough help. Besides, if the old people swarm you, you'll never make it home tonight."

"I guess you're right," sighed Caleb. "Merry Christmas. See you in a few weeks."

"Merry Christmas," replied Daniel as he slammed

the door and ran inside the building almost slipping on the ice laden sidewalk. The sight of his bumbling friend made Caleb chuckle as he drove off.

Daniel walked inside the lobby and past the couches that made the living room setting. He shot through the dining area and out a side door, once again facing the cold. After glancing into the front parking lot and making sure his buddy had left, he jumped back on the road and walked up the hill until over the horizon he could see a prison half a mile down into the valley. Pulling his hat down over his frozen ears, he trudged down the road through the crunchy snow, until finally arriving at the one place he didn't want to be.

"Your name?" asked the guard behind the glass laden desk.

"Daniel, Daniel Harris."

"You are just on time. The rest of your family is already inside," said the guard. "Follow me. I'll take you to them."

Daniel followed the large man through several locked doors, until finally arriving at a room where sat his parents, his younger brother, and Mr. Barrow. His mother immediately greeted him with a hug and a kiss on the cheek. "I was worried you weren't going to make it."

Daniel looked past his mother and over towards his father. "The car broke down. I had to catch a ride." His father nodded and was about to speak when Daniel's brother spoke up, "Hello Bolt."

Daniel took a moment to swallow the lump in his throat, "Hello Matthew."

Chapter 10

ACCOUNTABILITY

Thursday – July 5, 1990
3:38 PM
Southern Fork Trail

ALEX looked into the darkness of the night sky and then down to his trembling hands and cold, sweat-laden body. He had stripped down to his shorts hours ago and would put a shirt back on if not for the mad fever that rushed through his body. Uncomfortable with anything too close to his skin, he instead chose to wrestle with his sleeping bag; jumping in and out as his fits determined such. "Sorry I took so long," said Will as he emerged from the darkened woods. "The water filter is a bit stiff. It appears I need to clean it." As the apology reached Alex's ears, a bottle of water wet his lips and a cool, wet bandana chilled his forehead. He soon felt his shaky hands stabilizing in Will's powerful grip. The fears he had several hours ago when his sickened body began to react to the detoxing effects were now subsided by faith that his friend would not leave him. And with that one comforting thought he allowed his brain to fade.

When he awoke it was the next afternoon. He looked down to see that the shakes had left his body. Though his sleeping bag was soaked in sweat, not a drop rested on his skin. "Good morning," greeted Will. The look on his smiling face was evidence of how bad the night had been. "Are you hungry?"

"Morning? What time is it?"

"I've got 3:45 PM, but it's your morning nonetheless." Alex slowly started to get up, but then as the aches and dizziness hit him, he decided to lie back down. "Easy, buddy," said Will as he steadied his patient. "You've gone almost two days without eating. Let's take your recovery one step at a time."

Alex nodded as he scooted his body over to the nearest tree and sat against it. "I guess I'm not hiking today... or possibly tomorrow."

"That's okay. We have food and lots of entertainment."

"Entertainment? I'm not really feeling like a song and dance."

"But, we could talk," said Will. "I know you have a story and I'm betting it is a good one."

"No one wants to hear my story," muttered Alex as he looked away.

"I do. And since I've saved your life twice, you owe me a story."

The rest of the evening and throughout much of the night Alex shared his story. His childhood, his parent's divorce, the fight and the drug use; he shared it all until he was completely transparent. While Will listened, he too shared about his life and the many downturns that led to him escaping to the trail. Their conversation continued on for weeks and weeks until the day came when they stood atop Mount Oglethorpe.

"I think I'm looking forward to college," said Alex as they stared across the landscape they had traversed.

"You might as well," laughed Will. "I'm going to be on your case until you graduate."

"If you are letting me crash at your place, I guess you can stay on my case. It's not too late to back out though. Once we step off the trail it's final."

"I'm positive. Like I said, I inherited the house from my grandmother and it's only a few blocks from the college. Besides, I decided several miles ago that I was moving back there anyway. There's a juvenile facility nearby and I plan on working there."

"You want to work with teens?"

"I do. They have hope. Speaking of which, what are you hoping to major in?"

Alex reached up and touched the cross around his neck, "I may have something in mind."

Friday – January 14, 2011
6:12 PM
The Christian Student Center
at Big State University

The Christian Student Center bustled with activity as freshmen and others returned from their Christmas break and joined in the festivities of the Welcome Back gathering. New faces along with old swirled together as several took the opportunity to witness the new spirit that they had heard about all across campus.

From a second floor stairwell, Jess and Andrea looked below at the mingling of the masses. "I've never seen this many people here at one time," remarked Andrea. "It's not the same place we ruled over last year."

"You're right," replied Jess. "Soon it will be a mob of brainless twits with no class. Look at that girl right there... clueless to how bad she looks."

Andrea stood there nodding, "I know. That poor..." She stopped herself as Rose suddenly walked up. The presence of her friend refocused her mind. "That poor girl. I'm going to go talk to her. Two weeks from now she is going to look amazing!"

Jess looked at Andrea rather dumfounded and then quickly glanced at Rose. "She's changing you. I remember when you were fun."

Andrea paused for a second as if in deep thought, then looked Jess straight in the eyes. "You're right. She has changed me for the better. And, what you remember of me being fun, was actually me being mean."

"Whatever," snapped Jess. "You can't change who you are at the core."

"Yes you can. You most definitely can! I've surrounded myself with people who care about me and want me to be better and I'm going to be better."

"Don't fool yourself. You've surrounded yourself with losers because you are a loser and you will always be a loser."

As Jess's hateful words hung in the air Andrea stared at her solemnly at first, but then a slow smile stretched across her face. "Wow. Mr. Barrow was right. Your words hold no power whatsoever. Don't worry though. We haven't given up on you," and with that said, she walked over to Rose. "Ready?" Rose nodded and the two strolled down the stairs meeting Lisa halfway. "Let's get to work." With welcoming smiles the trio melted into the pool of new faces.

Monday – January 17, 2011
4:15 PM
Sunrise Youth Development Center

William Barrow sat in his office adjusting his old tin watch. Its materialistic value was miniscule and considering the daily attention it required any typical person would have chunked it long ago. For him though, it was a constant reminder of all the other people in his life who simply needed a little special care to keep going.

In the corner of his office sat Benjamin, ever so quietly. For the past several weeks his school work had suffered and his counseling sessions had reached an impasse. If Mr. Barrow couldn't solve the situation soon, Benjamin's course of treatment would take a turn towards drastic measures, beyond Mr. Barrow's influence.

"Benjamin, is there any way I can get you to talk with me today? We've already had two sessions of silence." Benjamin simply shook his head and looked away. "That's what I thought. In that case, I'm going to start a session with another student, so I can make the most of my day." Mr. Barrow then picked up his radio, "Send him in." Within moments the door opened and a guard escorted Matthew into the room. "Have a seat. Please ignore the mute in the corner...simply decoration." Matthew glanced at Benjamin, smiled and sat down. "If you don't mind, talk to me about how things are going with your family since our meeting right before Christmas."

"Things are going well...really well. My parents have been visiting regularly and we no longer talk about the bad night. Instead they are talking about starting me in a new school when I get out, and taking steps to get ready for college. It's nice."

"And how are things with your older brother, Daniel?"

Matthew took a deep breath and then slowly smiled again. "Of all people, I didn't think he would ever forgive me. For months all I could picture was his wrath when he caught me that night. I knew I had not only disappointed him, but disgraced him afterwards. Everyone looked at him differently after this all blew up. Whatever honor he had amongst his peers, I destroyed it for him."

"So what was his reaction that night when we all met?"

"He forgave me, and not only that; he apologized. He said he overreacted when he caught me that night and told me it was really small beans in comparison to some of the things he had done. He apologized for not being there for me afterwards when I got caught up in his old gang. It was not what I was expecting. He wasn't what I was expecting."

"What do you mean?"

"Before he was always on the verge of anger, like he

could blow up at any moment. Now he is mellowed, as if he has found what he is looking for. It's nice."

"Well whoop-dee-doo!" exploded Benjamin from the corner of the room. "You have a happy family to go home to! Congratulations!"

"Benjamin, do you want to talk to us about your family?" prodded Mr. Barrow.

"My family? My family is dead! Died in a car wreck that I caused. That's my family story."

"How did you cause the car to wreck?" interjected Matthew. "You can't drive."

Benjamin now looked down to the ground, "I was bothering my sister, Rose, and my father who was driving turned and yelled at me to quit. That's when he lost control and wrecked."

"That's not what caused the wreck," shared Mr. Barrow as he pulled a newspaper article out of Benjamin's file. "Your car was hit by an out of control semi. There was nothing your father could have done to prevent it. It was no one's fault, especially not yours."

Benjamin took the article and sat there quietly sobbing. Several minutes of silence passed before he finally muttered, "Still doesn't change the fact that I have no one to go home to. Once I leave here I'm on my own."

"That's why you've shut down?" asked Mr. Barrow. "You want to stay here?"

"I don't want to stay here...I just don't want to go out there. I have no one beyond those gates."

"You have your sister Rose," pointed out Mr. Barrow.

"She has her own life in college. My interference would just destroy her chance of moving on."

"You and I are friends, right?" asked Matthew.

"You are my only friend."

"What makes him your friend?" asked Mr. Barrow.

Benjamin sat quietly for a second collecting his thoughts. "He accepts me for who I am. He always believes in me and never says or does anything to hurt me. He has my back, no matter what."

"You two do have a special friendship forged through tough measures. Let me point out one thing true friends with close bonds are capable of doing," said Mr. Barrow as he focused in on Matthew. "True friends tell each other the deal no matter if it's painful or not."

Matthew stared at Mr. Barrow for a moment and then back at Benjamin. "I'm here for only a few more weeks and then I'm leaving. If you don't stop this foolishness and start doing your treatment, then you are going to be here alone, and I won't be able to protect you. Even worse, you're on your way to being sent to Block D where only the mentally deranged go, and there's no coming back from that. Do your treatment and get out of here!"

"So I can go to another foster home where they fear or ignore me?"

"If you do your treatment, I will have you out of here in a month and sent to foster care, but I don't think the Harris family will ignore or fear you."

"The Harris family?"

"Back before Christmas Mr. Barrow had a talk with my family and convinced them to become foster parents," smiled Matthew.

"All the legalities should be done by the time you are

ready to leave this place. Since I'm your counselor, it's my job to approve and oversee your post-lock up placement and treatment."

Benjamin tried to smile, but to look at it you would never know under the uncontrollable tears that ran down his face. Matthew looked at him and shook his head, "I don't care how much you cry, you're stuck with my old room and I'm taking over Daniel's room."

Friday, January 14, 2011
6:32 PM
Big State University

Daniel strolled down the sidewalk through the brisk air until he reached the Christian Student Center with a big sign that said, "Welcome One and All". He had helped in the planning and preparation for tonight's gathering, and was now running late in hosting duties. As he opened the door and entered, he was amazed at the mass crowd that had already gathered. "Hey Daniel!" greeted Lisa from the midway across the room. He turned on his greeting mode and started shaking hands and greeting others until finally he made it to her location. "Nice sweater. I'm guessing it was a Christmas gift?"

"Yes, does it look stupid? I knew I should have gone with the button down."

"It looks fine," smiled Lisa as she adjusted his collar. "Have you heard from Caleb?"

"No," replied Daniel. "We were supposed to meet here. Has he not arrived?"

"I haven't seen him. He could be running late."

"Among his shortcomings punctuality is not one of them. He's actually almost obsessive about it."

"Try calling him."

As Daniel reached for his phone a wave of guilt hit him having not contacted his friend throughout Christmas break. *I am the worst friend ever,* he thought as his phone rang without an answer. "He's not answering."

"Well go look for your friend," said Lisa. "We've got plenty of hosts tonight."

Daniel walked around the Center perusing the crowd, but when he found no sign of his friend, he left and headed towards the dorms. It didn't take him long to make it to Caleb's door and start knocking. "I see the light is on and I know you are there."

A minute later Caleb opened the door. "I guess this campus is too small to hide out." Daniel ignored the comment and greeted his friend with a hug that lifted him off the ground. "I missed you and so did everyone else. They're waiting on you at the Center."

"I'm not feeling very social tonight," replied Caleb. "Still shaking off the Christmas blues."

Daniel got quiet for a moment and then had a seat on Caleb's desk. "You miss your mother."

Caleb stared at him for a second, then wrinkled his brow, "How do you know about my mother? We've never talked about my family."

"You're Caleb Williams. Everyone in the surrounding counties who watched the news this summer knows about your family. Besides, I thought I was your closest friend. Shouldn't you be able to talk to me about your mother's death?"

Caleb continued to stare Daniel down, but no longer angrily. It was more of a solemn look. "You're right. I've not wanted to talk about it and since you never shared much about your family, I kind of found comfort in not having to go there."

"You can go there with me," said Daniel as he moved to a more comfortable chair. "That is what I'm here for."

With those words, Caleb let down a wall that he had been building since that horrible night. For the next hour Caleb shared everything he had been feeling, from sadness and regret for not taking the ride with his mother, to hatred for those who had senselessly gunned her down. Tears rolled down his eyes for the first time. Daniel sat silently and listened intently, while the whole time his heart became heavier with his own secret burden. After some time, Caleb grew quiet and relaxed, as if he had just freed himself from a heavy weight. "Thanks for listening to me," he said as he wiped the tears from his eyes.

Daniel now looked up with tears in his eyes. "Since tonight the veils are coming off, there is something I need to share with you. That night my car broke down. I didn't really go to my grandmother's place."

Caleb looked at him confused. "I dropped you off at the old folk's home."

"Yes, but then I walked half a mile down to Sunrise Youth Development Center."

"The juvy pen?"

"Yeah, that's where my brother is locked up."

"And you thought that I would judge you or look

down on you just because your brother has some troubles? I'm a better friend than that."

"That's not exactly what I was hiding from you," said Daniel as he took a deep breath. "My brother is Matthew Harris, one of the Brookhaven bravos."

As the words sank in Caleb went cold. The room began to spin and he fell backwards on his bed. "No, no, no..." he muttered over and over while he struggled with the reality he now faced. "Your brother killed my mother?"

"No!" cried Daniel. "He never touched the gun. He was just at the wrong place at the wrong time."

"But was a member of their gang? Your brother?"

"No, he wasn't. They grabbed him because they were looking for me."

"You were a member of their gang? exclaimed Caleb in utter confusion.

"Yes... I mean... I never would have done such a thing... and neither did my brother!"

"So you had nothing to do with it?"

"No!" yelled Daniel at the top of his lungs, but then he remembered the gun. "I mean...maybe."

Caleb grabbed his hair and started heading towards the door. Daniel followed, grabbing his arm. Caleb immediately fought back punching him in the face and knocking him to the ground. "Get away from me!" frantically screamed Caleb and then like a madman he ran out the door.

Friday – January 14, 2011
10:08 PM
The Christian Student Center
at Big State University

Alexander George sat quietly in his office. The festivities of the night had finally wrapped and it was now that rare time at the Center when silence ruled. Alex soaked it in and leaned back in his desk. He had almost cleared his mind of the day's clutter when his phone began to ring. Slipping back into minister mode he picked it up. "Hello, you've reached the Christian Student Center."

"Hey Alex... I mean, Mr. George."

"Hello Will, I mean, Mr. Barrow."

"How did the gathering go tonight?"

"It went great – a major turn around from when I first arrived. All the work we put into last semester is already paying off. We welcomed more students than I could count."

"Glad to hear it. Are we still on for dinner next Thursday night? I have a couple issues I need to talk to you about and get your advice."

"Same here, and yes, I wouldn't miss it."

"Excellent. Good night old friend."

"Good night." Alex set the phone down and smiled. Ever since that hiking trip he could always depend on Will to be there for him, and that had made all the difference in his life.

Not wanting to hang around for the next phone call, Alex gathered his usual belongings along with his coat and turned towards the door just in time to be startled by a lone figure standing there. Alex caught his breath and then took a closer look. "Caleb?"

"I saw the light on and... I didn't realize you were leaving." Caleb turned and began to walk away. Alex noticed immediately the swollen eyes and tears streaming down his face.

"Come back here, Caleb. I'm here now, and I'm not going anywhere." Caleb walked back in the room and at Alex's suggestion, had a seat. "What's wrong?"

"Daniel lied to me... he betrayed me...and I want to kill him!"

"I truly doubt you want to kill your closest friend."

"He's not my friend! Not anymore."

Alex sat down next to Daniel and looked him in the eyes, "I've watched the two of you closely these past few months and I know without doubt there are no two other students here closer. Your relationship has been one that others covet. You've been our living example of Jonathan and David. I doubt whatever happened tonight moved your relationship from that to arch enemies."

"He and his brother are a part of the same gang that killed my mother!" yelled Caleb.

Alex took a deep breath, "I know."

"What do you mean, you knew? Did everyone except me know?"

"To be honest, I thought you two had discussed this."

"Yeah, like, 'Hey my buddies and I killed your mom. Do you want to be friends?'"

In his heart, Alex wanted to defend Daniel and point out all the reasons why the death of Caleb's mother had nothing to do with him, but his mind knew that wasn't the route to take; not at this moment.

"I'm so sorry your mother died," he said looking into Caleb's eyes. "It's not fair and it's not right. You have every reason to be angry." Whether it was the right words or not, it was the permission that Caleb had wanted to cry out, and that's what he did that night. Alex gave up on time and simply surrendered the night to Caleb's wounded heart. At times they talked, and at times they gave way to emotions that could not be harnessed in words. Alex waited late into the night though, long after Caleb had exhausted his rage, before he mentioned Daniel again. As a lead in, he shared a personal story of a kid Caleb's age who betrayed another while on a long journey. He spoke about how he lied and stole, but in the end was forgiven.

"I'm sorry Mr. George," said Caleb as he continued to wipe his tear stained face, "but stealing is one thing. This is another. I don't think I can so easily forgive him."

Alex nodded in understanding, "Then let me share one last true story with you. "You and I are no different than Daniel. There was a time when we lied and betrayed He who would be our closest friend and ally. Because of us, our Friend had to lose His Son, yet He forgave us. We didn't deserve it, but His love was too great to do anything less."

Chapter 11

AFTERMATH

Saturday – February 12, 2011
11:20 am
The Christian Student Center
at Big State University

"IS this not the dullest combination of colors you have ever seen?" complained Andrea as she brought more buckets of paint into the study room that was receiving a much needed facelift. Several rooms had been remodeled over Christmas break to mirror the new spirit at the Christian Student Center. The study room was one of the last steps in the refurbishing process.

"No, I believe the colors will look just fine once everything is in place," replied Rose as she and Caleb worked on putting up the base coat.

"It's good someone has faith," snipped Andrea as she dropped the buckets and walked out. Rose just shook her head and continued painting. Caleb had been working quietly most of the morning, but finally put his brush down and turned to Rose.

"Can I ask you a question?"

"You want to know how I can continue to put up with Andrea even though she drives people crazy?" smiled Rose as she worked her roller.

"Pretty much," chuckled Caleb.

"There are some days I ask myself the same question," said Rose with a slight giggle. "She has her faults, but don't we all? In the big scheme of things, she has my best interest at heart and that means a lot to me. Besides, if it is an annoying Andrea day, I have other friends to turn to for encouragement. In that sense, she bonds many of us together."

"Interesting way to look at it," replied Caleb. "So, on Mr. Barrow's relationship scale you are...?"

"We are all over the scale depending on mine and Andrea's mood. In the last couple months we have started moving into the Action zone. She is one whom I can depend on. There was an instance last week when I was so frustrated with her that I was barely holding onto the Acceptance stage, but we made up and once the air was clear, we moved back to the Admiration level. Like Mr. Barrow said, relationships are fluid. We are all changing and growing."

"Excellent answer," said Caleb as he continued to paint.

"I'm glad you liked it," said Rose just as Daniel walked in the room with a paint brush in hand. He took one look at Caleb and without missing a step turned around and walked out. Rose watched the entire awkward moment and then looked at Caleb. "Now may I ask you a question?"

"Shoot."

"What's up with you and Daniel? You ran around here like bffs and now suddenly you don't talk to one another. What gives?"

Caleb shrugged, "It's complicated."

Rose stopped painting and stared him down. "That is such a pansy answer. Come on. Man up. Spill it."

"You wouldn't understa..."

"Seriously? You do know I lost both my parents two years ago? I also have a younger brother locked up right now. I'm friends with Andrea! Try me."

"I'm sorry," replied Caleb in surprise.

"Water under the bridge. Why are you mad at Daniel?"

"He and his brother were involved with the guys who murdered my mother."

"Involved as in, they held her down as she was shot, or involved as in, they knew the guys?"

"You're pretty harsh!"

"I'm sorry. I'm trying to work on that issue. The past years have toughened my skin and sometimes I forget how to be gentle."

"Well, to answer your question, Daniel had once been a member of their gang and had not told me."

"So you're mad because he once ran with these thugs at an earlier point in his life?"

"No, I mean yes... I'm mad because he didn't tell me."

"I see," replied Rose as she picked up the roller and got back to work."

"Are you not going to give me advice now about how I should forgive him?"

Rose shook her head. "I asked a question and you answered it. That was the deal. I don't have any influence over you and it doesn't sound like you need my advice anyway."

Caleb stared at her for a brief moment and then went back to work only to stop a few seconds later. "Did you ever forgive the people who killed your parents?"

Rose continued to work the roller. "You mean the driver who lost control of his truck and struck our car? The man who left me as an orphan with a terrible scar on my face? Yes. I forgave him."

"Why?"

"The hatred I had for him was more than I could bear. I had to turn it lose. I know it's cliché, but life is too short. I had things to do besides sit around and pout about my rough life. You now owe me two questions."

"That is correct."

"The first question is, how did you know I wanted you to buy me lunch at the Sandwich King? And, how did you know that Combo #3 is my favorite?"

Tuesday – February 22, 2011
4:50 PM
The Track at Big State University

"Good workout today!" barked the tubby coach. "Don't forget our first meet is this weekend. While I can only take the top runners on the van, I know the rest of you will be tagging along to cheer them on. I believe

Max is the mastermind behind our non-school sanctioned caravan?"

"Yes sir, coach," said Max. "Off the record, Tommy and I are both driving and will be happy to take everyone else." After the coach finished dismissing the team, Max wandered over to a plot of grass and began his cool-down stretches. He usually did them inside the locker room with the rest of the team, but during the last month conversation had grown cold and rather awkward on the team. With Caleb and Daniel no longer speaking to one another, the mood on the team had become uncomfortable.

"Hey Max," quietly greeted Daniel as he walked up from behind.

Max turned, but wasn't surprised by Daniel's presence. "Are you dodging the rest of the guys as well?"

"No...I mean, sort of." Daniel sat down next to Max so he could look him in the eyes. "I came here to tell you get ready to compete this weekend."

"What are you talking about?"

"I'm quitting the team and you are next in line to take my place on the relay team."

"You can't quit the team!" exclaimed Max. "I know things are weird between you and Caleb, but that's no reason to quit!"

"If I don't quit, he will and the team is better with him than me."

"Can you guys not just get over it?"

"I would love to have this behind us, but I don't think he can let it go." Daniel stood up and began to walk off. "Anyway, I'm about to go have a short talk with Coach."

"Hold up!" yelled Max as he hopped up and darted over to Daniel. "Give me 24 hours to talk to Caleb."

Daniel stopped and shook his head. "No offense, but you don't have a lot of pull with him and he is a rather strong willed fellow."

"I know he doesn't like me, but I have known him longer than anyone else on the team. Just give me 24 hours."

Daniel stared Max in the eyes and finally nodded, "Alright. Talk to you tomorrow."

Tuesday – February 22, 2011
6:20 PM
Cafeteria at Big State University

Tuesday nights were always pasta night in the cafeteria. One could still go to the five other bars and eat everything from Mexican to Chinese, but on Tuesday nights the pasta bar was the freshest and best. It was one fact Caleb knew about college life and during these confusing days he held tightly to those truths.

He sat quietly eating in a section of the cafeteria he normally never frequented. It had been a part of his new strategy during the past month to eliminate Daniel from his life. He was learning, though, that uprooting a close friend was harder than he first thought. The roots ran deep.

From where he sat he could see Lisa, Andrea, and half a dozen guys and girls from the CSC. Lance was in the group and from Caleb's viewpoint it seemed he finally was catching on to the whole friendship deal. Caleb wanted to join them, but knew if Daniel walked in he would have to make an awkward exodus. Instead he silently finished his meal and slipped out before anyone could see him.

Tonight he had studying to do, but on his way back to his dorm, his feet wandered down to the track. It was where he liked to think. He walked up to the bleachers where he first saw Daniel run and had a seat. He had spent many hours here reflecting on his past. It was also where, when he saw Daniel fighting for recognition, it recharged his spirit. How fitting that it was now where he found himself torn and broken.

"Caleb, we need to talk," said Max as he walked up from behind.

"I'm guessing you don't want advice on jumping out of the blocks."

"I'm not here for advice," said Max as he sat down next to him.

"Are you here to beat me again? I don't see the old gang."

"I'm here asking you to not destroy this team."

"I have no plans of destroying anything."

"Well, that's exactly what you are doing! Daniel almost quit today and if you don't do anything about it, he will quit tomorrow."

"I have no control over Daniel," snapped Caleb as he tried to get up, but Max pulled him back down.

"Look Caleb. As much as I didn't like you in high school, the fact is I love this team and you are the heart of it. These guys have become my family and that started when you joined the team."

"I love this team too!" yelled Caleb. "Daniel and I just have an issue!"

"And that issue, whatever it is, is a big cancer to our group. Can you guys not work it out? You can't hate him more than you hated me!"

Caleb glared at him. "I did hate you for quite some time."

"But somewhere along the way you got over it."

"Yeah. I guess since I never liked you, you were only able to wound me skin deep. When I came here and decided to join the team, I decided to start new with you. I still don't trust you, but I don't hate you."

Silence set in between the two as they allowed the word to settle. If was several seconds before the peaceful pause was broken. "Since we're being honest, when your mother died, I felt terrible about beating you," confessed Max. "I did it out of jealousy. I do regret it."

"That's nice to know," shrugged Caleb.

"You really don't hate me?" asked Max.

"No."

"But you still don't like me?"

"That's correct."

"So, I'm growing on you?" smiled Max.

"Yeah, you could say that," chuckled Caleb before getting serious again. "Daniel is seriously about to quit the team?"

"He meets with the coach tomorrow after practice. He said he was afraid you would quit if he stays on the team and he believes you are more important to the team."

"I see."

"Can you work some of your Caleb magic and solve

this problem without hurting our team? I hate to say this, but you'll be my hero if you can do that."

"Thanks for talking to me. I'll see what I can do."

Wednesday – February 23, 2011
4:22 PM
The Track at Big State University

Where is he? thought Max as he finished his three mile run for the day. The coach had relaxed on them today and let everyone run their own three mile distance for practice. Max had run with most of the team including Daniel. Now he watched as Daniel prepared to head to the coach's office. "No word from Caleb today?" asked Max.

Daniel shook his head and looked around, "No and from the looks of it he may have already quit the team."

Max didn't know what to say, so he simply muttered an "I'm sorry," and walked off. Daniel finished cooling off and then headed to the one place he didn't want to go. From the track, the coach's office was down the corridor under the stadium, just before reaching the weight room. The walk seemed to take forever and the ten second pause before he opened the door was an additional eternity, but finally he knocked and entered. Behind the desk with his feet up sat Caleb.

"Are you the new coach?" asked Daniel in a bit of shock.

"No," calmly replied Caleb. "But being captain does have its privileges."

"Okay," replied Daniel as he turned to walk out.

"I'm sorry," said Caleb as he hopped up from his seat. "I'm sorry I've been a jerk."

Daniel stopped and turned around. "I deserve no better. No matter how I try to escape it, I'm trash. The gun I gave those guys killed your mother. No matter how much I don't want to admit it, I had a part in her death just like I had a part in my brother's incarceration. I deserve far worse treatment than what you have given me. I deserve death!"

"You are not trash," said Caleb. "You are my closest friend, or at least I want you to be. You had no more to do with her death than I did. Those guys would have gotten a gun whether it was yours or not. If I had just shared with her that night how I had just been beaten, she would have at least not left at that moment and likely never have run into those thugs. I was too ashamed to tell her."

"It's not your fault," said Daniel as he placed his hand on Caleb's shoulder. "You had no idea what was about to happen."

"You can't live with the guilt either," replied Caleb. You are not the guy you were in high school. I forgive you. Please forgive me for treating you so badly this past month. I just had to work it out."

"I never held your reaction against you," shared Daniel with tears in his eyes. "Your friendship was a blessing I didn't deserve."

"You're wrong. You deserve even better, and I'm going to be better, if you will let me."

Daniel replied but it was muffled as he buried his face in Caleb with a long hug. After a few minutes of non-macho behavior, the two collected themselves . "I've never survived a break-up before. What's the next step?" asked Daniel.

"I don't know, but if you could eat with me in the cafeteria that would be great. It's lonely over in the corner."

Saturday – February 26, 2010
12:20 PM
The Track at Some Other University

"If I vomit, can you run for me?" asked Daniel as he perused the crowd that had come to watch him and fifteen other teams compete. The track looked the same as the one back at BSU, but the atmosphere was electrified with immense anticipation.

Max started laughing, "That's right! You never competed in high school. This is your first track meet. Well virgin, vomiting is par for the course on race day. You would have to pass out right before the race for me to take your place, and not afterwards, which is also par for the course."

Daniel just looked at him and turned even whiter, "I'll be right back...maybe."

As he darted off, Caleb walked up. "Is he okay?"

Max nodded, "Just some freshman jitters. How are you feeling?"

Caleb took a deep breath, "I'm good."

"You better be. If you run anything short of your best I will be gunning for your position next week."

"You better be gunning for my position anyway," chuckled Caleb.

The next several hours passed by fast as each sprinter ran his race to the applause of the audience. Their round little coach bounced around the track from one event to the next sometimes screaming, sometimes cheering, but always in motion. When it was all said and done, the team had done exceptionally well for their first meet. Caleb had won the 400 meters and along with Daniel, Reed, and Billy, they won the mile relay race.

Throughout the meet, several students from the CSC had cheered them on. They even had a banner with each runner's name on it. After it was over, a number of them came down to the track to congratulate them. "You guys were great!" said Lisa as she gave Daniel a hug.

"I guess fifth isn't bad for my first meet. It gives me something to work towards," replied Daniel humbly as Andrea, Rose and a young man approached.

"Sure, and it wasn't bad when you moved your team from fourth to second during the relay race," said Andrea.

"Yeah, there was that."

"I want to introduce you to my brother, Benjamin," said Rose.

Benjamin walked up and shook his hand. "Well, finally we meet. Matthew isn't being too rough on you is he?"

"I just got out this past week, but so far he's bearable."

"If he starts talking too much smack, you have my permission to shut him down."

"I will not fail you Oh Captain My Captain," smiled

Benjamin. "I wanted to say your parents are amazing people for taking me in."

"Are my parents here?" asked Daniel.

"They're over there speaking to your teammate." Daniel turned around to see his family approach Caleb.

"I'm Daniel's father and I want you to know you are an excellent runner."

"Thank you, sir," replied Caleb.

"And we are so thankful for you being such a good friend to Daniel," said Daniel's mother. "You mean the world to him and therefore you mean the world to us."

"I appreciate that ma'am."

"You are welcome at our house anytime and your attendance is expected at every holiday, including your birthday which is coming up soon!"

"I will definitely be there," laughed Caleb.

"Okay, we've got to go talk to our other son now." As they walked off Caleb looked over at Daniel who gave a look to say, "I apologize for my parents." Caleb laughed again and when he turned around another young man was standing in front of him.

"Mr. Williams, you ran an incredible race."

Caleb's previous face of laughter quieted to a soft smile. "Thank you. Are you Daniel's brother?"

"Yes sir."

"Nice to meet you, Matthew. You can call me Caleb."